Kishen Bhagavan
Los Altos, CA
Dec 1, 2002

DIALOGUES ON MATHEMATICS

DIALOGUES
ON MATHEMATICS

ALFRÉD RÉNYI

Mathematical Institute
Hungarian Academy of Sciences

HOLDEN-DAY

San Francisco, Cambridge, London, Amsterdam

Originally published as *Dialógusok a matematikáról* by Akadémiai Kiadó, Budapest, 1965.

PICTURE CREDITS

The Bettman Archive: pages 28, 50
The British Museum: page 2
The Mount Wilson and Palomar Observatories: page 62
Soprintendenze alle Antichita dell'Etruria Meridionale: page 40

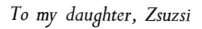

To my daughter, Zsuzsi

CONTENTS

A SOCRATIC DIALOGUE
ON MATHEMATICS

SOCRATES

A SOCRATIC DIALOGUE ON MATHEMATICS

SOCRATES   Are you looking for somebody, my dear Hippocrates?

HIPPOCRATES   No, Socrates, because I have already found him, namely you. I have been looking for you everywhere. Somebody told me at the agora that he saw you walking here along the River Ilissos; so I came after you.

SOCRATES   Well then, tell me why you came, and then I want to ask you something about our discussion with Protagoras. Do you still remember it?

HIPPOCRATES   How can you ask? Since that time not a single day has passed without my thinking about it. I came today to ask your advice because that discussion was on my mind.

SOCRATES   It seems, my dear Hippocrates, that you want to talk to me about the very question I wish to discuss with you; thus the two subjects are one and the same. It seems that the mathematicians are mistaken in saying that two is never equal to one.

HIPPOCRATES   As a matter of fact, Socrates, mathematics is just the topic I want to talk to you about.

SOCRATES   Hippocrates, you certainly know that I am not a mathematician. Why did you not take your questions to the celebrated Theodoros?

HIPPOCRATES   You are amazing, Socrates, you answer my questions even before I tell you what they are. I came to ask your opinion about my becoming a pupil of Theodoros. When I came to you the last time, with the intention of becoming a pupil of Protagoras, we went to him together and you directed the discussion so that it became quite clear that he did not know the subject he taught. Thus I changed my mind and did not follow him. This discussion helped me to see what I should not do, but did not show me what I should do. I am still wondering about this. I visit banquets and the palaestra with young men of my age, I dare say I have a pleasant time, but this does not satisfy me. It disturbs me to feel myself ignorant. More precisely, I feel that the knowledge I have is rather uncertain. During the discussion with Protagoras, I realized that my knowledge about familiar notions like virtue, justice and courage was far from satisfactory. Nevertheless, I think it is great progress that I now see clearly my own ignorance.

SOCRATES   I am glad, my dear Hippocrates, that you understand me so well. I always tell myself quite frankly that I know nothing. *The difference between me and most other people is that I do not imagine I know what in reality I do not know.*

HIPPOCRATES   This clearly shows your wisdom, Socrates. But such knowledge is not enough for me. I have a strong desire to obtain some certain and solid knowledge, and I shall not be happy until I do. I am constantly pondering what kind of knowledge I should try to acquire. Recently, Theaitetos told me that certainty exists only in mathematics and suggested that I learn mathematics from his master, Theodoros, who is the leading expert on numbers and geometry in Athens. Now, I should not want to make the same mistake I made when I wanted to be a pupil of Protagoras. Therefore tell me, Socrates, shall I find the kind of sound knowledge I seek if I learn mathematics from Theodoros?

SOCRATES If you want to study mathematics, O son of Apollo-doros, then you certainly cannot do better than go to my highly esteemed friend Theodoros. But you must decide for yourself whether or not you really do want to study mathematics. Nobody can know your needs better than you yourself.

HIPPOCRATES Why do you refuse to help me, Socrates? Perhaps I offended you without knowing it?

SOCRATES You misunderstand me, my young friend. I am not angry; but you ask the impossible of me. Everybody must de-cide for himself what he wants to do. *I can do no more than assist as a midwife at the birth of your decision.*

HIPPOCRATES Please, my dear Socrates, do not refuse to help me, and if you are free now, let us start immediately.

SOCRATES Well, if you want to. Let us lie down in the shadow of that plane-tree and begin. *But first tell me, are you ready to conduct the discussion in the manner I prefer? I shall ask the questions and you shall answer them. By this method you will come to see more clearly what you already know, for it brings into blossom the seeds of knowledge already in your soul.* I hope you will not behave like King Darius who killed the master of his mines because he brought only copper out of a mine the king thought contained gold. I hope you do not forget that a miner can find in a mine only what it contains.

HIPPOCRATES I swear that I shall make no reproaches, but, by Zeus, let us begin mining at once.

SOCRATES All right. Then tell me, do you know what mathematics is? I suppose you can define it since you want to study it.

HIPPOCRATES I think every child could do so. Mathematics is one of the sciences, and one of the finest.

SOCRATES I did not ask you to praise mathematics, but to describe its nature. For instance, if I asked you about the art of physicians,

5

you would answer that this art deals with health and illness, and has the aim of healing the sick and preserving health. Am I right?

HIPPOCRATES Certainly.

SOCRATES Then answer me this: does the art of the physicians deal with something that exists or with something that does not exist? If there were no physicians, would illness still exist?

HIPPOCRATES Certainly, and even more than now.

SOCRATES Let us have a look at another art, say that of astronomy. Do you agree with me that astronomers study the motion of the stars?

HIPPOCRATES To be sure.

SOCRATES And if I ask you whether astronomy deals with something that exists, what is your answer?

HIPPOCRATES My answer is yes.

SOCRATES Would stars exist if there were no astronomers in the world?

HIPPOCRATES Of course. And if Zeus in his anger extinguished all mankind, the stars would still shine in the sky at night. But why do we discuss astronomy instead of mathematics?

SOCRATES Do not be impatient, my good friend. Let us consider a few other arts in order to compare them with mathematics. How would you describe the man who knows about all the creatures living in the woods or in the depths of the sea?

HIPPOCRATES He is a scientist studying living nature.

SOCRATES And do you agree that such a man studies things which exist?

HIPPOCRATES I agree.

SOCRATES And if I say that every art deals with something that exists, would you agree?

HIPPOCRATES Completely.

SOCRATES Now tell me, my young friend, what is the object of mathematics? What things does a mathematician study?

HIPPOCRATES I have asked Theaitetos the same question. He answered that a mathematician studies numbers and geometrical forms.

SOCRATES Well, the answer is right, but would you say that these things exist?

HIPPOCRATES Of course. How can we speak of them if they do not exist?

SOCRATES Then tell me, if there were no mathematicians, would there be prime numbers, and if so, where would they be?

HIPPOCRATES I really do not know what to answer. Clearly, if mathematicians think about prime numbers, then they exist in their consciousness; but if there were no mathematicians, the prime numbers would not be anywhere.

SOCRATES Do you mean that we have to say mathematicians study non-existing things?

HIPPOCRATES Yes, I think we have to admit that.

SOCRATES Let us look at the question from another point of view. Here, I wrote on this wax tablet the number 37. Do you see it?

HIPPOCRATES Yes, I do.

SOCRATES And can you touch it with your hand?

HIPPOCRATES Certainly.

SOCRATES Then perhaps numbers do exist?

HIPPOCRATES O Socrates, you are mocking me. Look here, I have drawn on the same tablet a dragon with seven heads. Does it follow that such a dragon exists? I have never met anybody who has seen a dragon, and I am convinced that dragons do not exist at all except in fairy tales. But suppose I am mistaken, suppose

7

somewhere beyond the pillars of Heracles dragons really do exist, that still has nothing to do with my drawing.

SOCRATES You speak the truth, Hippocrates, and I agree with you completely. But does this mean that even though we can speak about them, and write them down, numbers nevertheless do not exist in reality?

HIPPOCRATES Certainly.

SOCRATES Do not draw hasty conclusions. Let us make another trial. Am I right in saying that we can count the sheep here in the meadow or the ships in the harbor of Pireus?

HIPPOCRATES Yes, we can.

SOCRATES And the sheep and the ships exist?

HIPPOCRATES Clearly.

SOCRATES But if the sheep exist, their number must be something that exists, too?

HIPPOCRATES You are making fun of me, Socrates. Mathematicians do not count sheep; that is the business of shepherds.

SOCRATES Do you mean, what mathematicians study is not the number of sheep or ships, or of other existing things, but the number itself? And thus they are concerned with something that exists only in their minds?

HIPPOCRATES Yes, this is what I mean.

SOCRATES You told me that according to Theaitetos mathematicians study numbers and geometrical forms. How about forms? If I ask you whether they exist, what is your answer?

HIPPOCRATES Certainly they exist. We can see the form of a beautiful vessel, for example, and feel it with our hands, too.

SOCRATES Yet I still have one difficulty. If you look at a vessel what do you see, the vessel or its form?

HIPPOCRATES   I see both.

SOCRATES   Is that the same thing as looking at a lamb? Do you see the lamb and also its hair?

HIPPOCRATES   I find the simile very well chosen.

SOCRATES   Well, I think it limps like Hephaestus. You can cut the hair off the lamb and then you see the lamb without its hair, and the hair without the lamb. Can you separate in a similar way the form of a vessel from the vessel itself?

HIPPOCRATES   Certainly not, and I dare say nobody can.

SOCRATES   And nevertheless you still believe that you can see a geometric form?

HIPPOCRATES   I am beginning to doubt it.

SOCRATES   Besides this, if mathematicians study the forms of vessels, shouldn't we call them potters?

HIPPOCRATES   Certainly.

SOCRATES   Then if Theodoros is the best mathematician would he not be the best potter, too? I have heard many people praising him, but nobody has told me that he understands anything about pottery. I doubt whether he could make even the simplest pot. Or perhaps mathematicians deal with the form of statues or buildings?

HIPPOCRATES   If they did, they would be sculptors and architects.

SOCRATES   Well, my friend, we have come to the conclusion that mathematicians when studying geometry are not concerned with the forms of existing objects such as vessels, but with forms which exist only in their thoughts. Do you agree?

HIPPOCRATES   I have to agree.

SOCRATES   Having established that mathematicians are concerned with things that do not exist in reality, but only in their thoughts, let us examine the statement of Theaitetos, which you mentioned, that mathematics gives us more reliable and more trustworthy knowledge than does any other branch of science. Tell me, did Theaitetos give you some examples?

HIPPOCRATES   Yes, he said for instance that one cannot know exactly how far Athens is from Sparta. Of course, the people who travel that way agree on the number of days one has to walk, but it is impossible to know exactly how many feet the distance is. On the other hand, one can tell, by means of the theorem of Pythagoras, what the length of the diagonal of a square is. Theaitetos also said that it is impossible to give the exact number of people living in Hellas. If somebody tried to count all of them, he would never get the exact figure, because during the counting some old people would die and children would be born; thus the total number could be only approximately correct. But if you ask a mathematician how many edges a regular dodecahedron has, he will tell you that the dodecahedron is bounded by 12 faces, each having 5 edges. This makes 60, but as each edge belongs to two faces and thus has been counted twice, the number of edges of the dodecahedron is equal to 30, and this figure is beyond every doubt.

SOCRATES   Did he mention any other examples?

HIPPOCRATES   Quite a few, but I do not remember all of them. He said that in reality you never find two things which are exactly the same. No two eggs are exactly the same, even the pillars of Poseidon's temple are slightly different from each other; but one may be sure that the two diagonals of a rectangle are exactly equal. He quoted Heraclitus who said that everything which exists is constantly changing, and that sure knowledge is only possible about things which never change, for instance, the odd and the even, the straight line and the circle.

SOCRATES   That will do. These examples convince me that in mathematics we can get knowledge which is beyond doubt, while in other sciences or in everyday life it is impossible. Let us try to summarize the results of our inquiry into the nature of mathematics. Am I right in saying we came to the conclusion that mathematics studies non-existing things and is able to find out the full truth about them?

HIPPOCRATES   Yes, that is what we established.

SOCRATES   But tell me, for Zeus's sake, my dear Hippocrates, is it not mysterious that one can know more about things which do not exist than about things which do exist?

HIPPOCRATES   If you put it like that, it certainly is a mystery. I am sure there is some mistake in our arguments.

SOCRATES   No, we proceeded with the utmost care and we controlled every step of the argument. There cannot be any mistake in our reasoning. But listen, I remember something which may help us to solve the riddle.

HIPPOCRATES   Tell me quickly, because I am quite bewildered.

SOCRATES   This morning I was in the hall of the second archon, where the wife of a carpenter from the village Pitthos was accused of betraying and, with the aid of her lover, murdering her husband. The woman protested and swore to Artemis and Aphrodite that she was innocent, that she never loved anyone but her husband, and that her husband was killed by pirates. Many people were called as witnesses. Some said that the woman was guilty, others said that she was innocent. It was impossible to find out what really happened.

HIPPOCRATES   Are you mocking me again? First you confused me completely, and now instead of helping me to find the truth you tell me such stories.

SOCRATES   Do not be angry, my friend, I have serious reasons for speaking about this woman whose guilt it was impossible to ascertain. But one thing is sure. The woman exists. I saw her with my own eyes, and of anyone who was there, many of whom have never lied in their lives, you can ask the same question and you will receive the same answer.

HIPPOCRATES Your testimony is sufficient for me, my dear Socrates. Let it be granted that the woman exists. But what has this fact to do with mathematics?

SOCRATES More than you imagine. But tell me first, do you know the story about Agamemnon and Clytemnestra?

HIPPOCRATES Everybody knows the story. I saw the trilogy of Aeschylus at the theatre last year.

SOCRATES Then tell me the story in a few words.

HIPPOCRATES While Agamemnon, the king of Mycenae, fought under the walls of Troy, his wife, Clytemnestra, committed adultery with Aegisthus, the cousin of her husband. After the fall of Troy, when Agamemnon returned home, his wife and her lover murdered him.

SOCRATES Tell, me Hippocrates, is it quite sure that Clytemnestra was guilty?

HIPPOCRATES I do not understand why you ask me such questions. There can be no doubt about the story. According to Homer, when Odysseus visited the underworld he met Agamemnon, who told Odysseus his sad fate.

SOCRATES But are you sure that Clytemnestra and Agamemnon and all the other characters of the story really existed?

HIPPOCRATES Perhaps I would be ostracized if I said this in public, but my opinion is that it is impossible either to prove or disprove today, after so many centuries, whether the stories of Homer are true or not. But this is quite irrelevant. When I told you that Clytemnestra was guilty, I did not speak about the real Clytemnestra—if such a person ever lived—but about the Clytemnestra of our Homeric tradition, about the Clytemnestra in the trilogy of Aeschylus.

SOCRATES   May I say that we know nothing about the real Clytemnestra? Even her existence is uncertain, but as regards the Clytemnestra who is a character in the triology of Aeschylus, we are sure that she was guilty and murdered Agamemnon because that is what Aeschylus tells us.

HIPPOCRATES   Yes, of course. But why do you insist on all this?

SOCRATES   You will see in a moment. Let me summarize what we found out. It is impossible in the case of the flesh and blood woman who was tried today in Athens to establish whether she is guilty, while there can be no doubt about the guilt of Clytemnestra who is a character in a play and who probably never existed. Do you agree?

HIPPOCRATES   Now I am beginning to understand what you want to say. But it would be better if you drew the conclusions yourself.

SOCRATES   The conclusion is this: we have much more certain knowledge about persons who exist only in our imagination, for example about characters in a play, than about living persons. If we say that Clytemnestra was guilty, it means only that this is how Aeschylus imagined her and presented her in his play. The situation is exactly the same in mathematics. We may be sure that the diagonals of a rectangle are equal because this follows from the definition of a rectangle given by mathematicians.

HIPPOCRATES   Do you mean, Socrates, that our paradoxical result is really true and one can have a much more certain knowledge about non-existent things—for instance about the objects of mathematics—than about the real objects of nature? I think that now I also see the reason for this. The notions which we ourselves have created are by their very nature completely known to us, and we can find out the full truth about them because they have no other reality outside our imagination. However, the objects which exist in the real world are not identical with our picture of them, which is always incomplete and approximate; therefore our knowledge about these real things can never be complete or quite certain.

SOCRATES   That is the truth, my young friend, and you stated it better than I could have.

HIPPOCRATES   This is to your credit, Socrates, because you led me to understand these things. I see now not only that Theaitetos was quite right in telling me I must study mathematics if I want to obtain unfailing knowledge, but also why he was right. However, if you have guided me with patience up to now, please do not abandon me yet because one of my questions, in fact the most important one, is still unanswered.

SOCRATES   What is this question?

HIPPOCRATES   Please remember, Socrates, that I came to ask your advice as to whether I should study mathematics. You helped me to realize that mathematics and only mathematics can give me the sort of sound knowledge I want. But what is the use of this knowledge? It is clear that if one obtains some knowledge about the existing world, even if this knowledge is incomplete and is not quite certain, it is nevertheless of value to the individual as well as to the state. Even if one gets some knowledge about things such as the stars, it may be useful, for instance in navigation at night. But what is the use of knowledge of non-existing things such as that which mathematics offers? Even if it is complete and beyond any doubt, what is the use of knowledge concerning things which do not exist in reality?

SOCRATES   My dear friend, I am quite sure you know the answer, only you want to examine me.

HIPPOCRATES   By Heracles, I do not know the answer. Please help me.

SOCRATES   Well, let us try to find it. We have established that the notions of mathematics are created by the mathematician himself. Tell me, does this mean that the mathematician chooses his notions quite arbitrarily as it pleases him?

HIPPOCRATES   As I told you, I do not yet know much about mathematics. But it seems to me that the mathematician is as free to choose the objects of his study as the poet is free to choose the characters of his play, and as the poet invests his characters with whatever traits please him, so can the mathematician endow his notions with such properties as he likes.

SOCRATES   If this were so, there would be as many mathematical truths as there are mathematicians. How do you explain, then, that all mathematicians study the same notions and problems? How do you explain that, as often happens, mathematicians living far from each other and having no contact independently discover the same truths? I never heard of two poets writing the same poem.

HIPPOCRATES   Nor have I heard of such a thing. But I remember Theaitetos telling me about a very interesting theorem he discovered on incommensurable distances. He showed his results to his master, Theodoros, who produced a letter by Archytas in which the same theorem was contained almost word for word.

SOCRATES   In poetry that would be impossible. Now you see that there is a problem. But let us continue. How do you explain that the mathematicians of different countries can usually agree about the truth, while about questions concerning the state, for example, the Persians and the Spartans have quite opposite views from ours in Athens, and, moreover, we here do not often agree with each other?

HIPPOCRATES   I can answer that last question. In matters concerning the state everybody is personally interested, and these personal interests are often in contradiction. This is why it is difficult to

15

come to an agreement. However, the mathematician is led purely by his desire to find the truth.

SOCRATES   Do you mean to say that the mathematicians are trying to find a truth which is completely independent of their own person?

HIPPOCRATES   Yes, I do.

SOCRATES   But then we were mistaken in thinking that mathematicians choose the objects of their study at their own will. It seems that the object of their study has some sort of existence which is independent of their person. We have to solve this new riddle.

HIPPOCRATES   I do not see how to start.

SOCRATES   If you still have patience, let us try it together. Tell me, what is the difference between the sailor who finds an uninhabited island and the painter who finds a new color, one which no other painter has used before him?

HIPPOCRATES   I think that the sailor may be called a discoverer, and the painter an inventor. The sailor discovers an island which existed before him, only it was unknown, while the painter invents a new color which before that did not exist at all.

SOCRATES   Nobody could answer the question better. But tell me, the mathematician who finds a new truth, does he discover it or invent it? Is he a discoverer as the sailor or an inventor as the painter?

HIPPOCRATES   It seems to me that the mathematician is more like a discoverer. He is a bold sailor who sails on the unknown sea of thought and explores its coasts, islands and whirlpools.

SOCRATES   Well said, and I agree with you completely. I would add only that to a lesser extent the mathematician is an inventor too, especially when he invents new concepts. But every discoverer has to be, to a certain extent, an inventor too. For instance, if a sailor wants to get to places which other sailors before him were unable to reach, he has to build a ship that is better than the ships other sailors used. The new concepts invented by the mathematicians are like new ships which carry the discoverer farther on the great sea of thought.

HIPPOCRATES   My dear Socrates, you helped me to find the answer to the question which seemed so difficult to me. The main aim of the mathematician is to explore the secrets and riddles of the sea of human thought. These exist independently of the person of the mathematician, though not from humanity as a whole. The mathematician has a certain freedom to invent new concepts as tools, and it seems that he could do this at his discretion. However, he is not quite free in doing this because the new concepts have to be useful for his work. The sailor also can build any sort of ship at his discretion, but, of course, he would be mad to build a ship which would be crushed to pieces by the first storm. Now I think that everything is clear.

SOCRATES   If you see everything clearly, try again to answer the question: what is the object of mathematics?

HIPPOCRATES   We came to the conclusion that besides the world in which we live, there exists another world, the world of human thought, and the mathematician is the fearless sailor who explores this world, not shrinking back from the troubles, dangers and adventures which await him.

SOCRATES   My friend, your youthful vigor almost sweeps me off my feet, but I am afraid that in the ardor of your enthusiasm you overlook certain questions.

HIPPOCRATES   What are these questions?

SOCRATES   I do not want to disappoint you, but I feel that your main question has not yet been answered. We have not yet answered the question: what is the use of exploring the wonderful sea of human thought?

HIPPOCRATES You are right, my dear Socrates, as always. But won't you put aside your method this time and tell me the answer immediately?

SOCRATES No, my friend, even if I could, I would not do this, and it is for your sake. The knowledge somebody gets without work is almost worthless to him. We understand thoroughly only that which—perhaps with some outside help—we find out ourselves, just as a plant can use only the water which it sucks up from the soil through its own roots.

HIPPOCRATES All right, let us continue our search by the same method, but at least help me by a question.

SOCRATES Let us go back to the point where we established that the mathematician is not dealing with the number of sheep, ships or other existing things, but with the numbers themselves. Don't you think, however, that what the mathematicians discover to be true for pure numbers is true for the number of existing things too? For instance, the mathematician finds that 17 is a prime number. Therefore, is it not true that you cannot distribute 17 living sheep to a group of people, giving each the same number, unless there are 17 people?

HIPPOCRATES Of course, it is true.

SOCRATES Well, how about geometry? Can it not be applied in building houses, in making pots or in computing the amount of grain a ship can hold?

HIPPOCRATES Of course, it can be applied, though it seems to me that for these practical purposes of the craftsman not too much mathematics is needed. The simple rules known already by the clerks of the pharaohs in Egypt are sufficient for most such purposes, and the new discoveries about which Theaitetos spoke to me with such overflowing fervor are neither used nor needed in practice.

SOCRATES Perhaps not at the moment, but they may be used in the future.

HIPPOCRATES I am interested in the present.

SOCRATES If you want to be a mathematician, you must realize you will be working mostly for the future. Now, let us return to the main question. We saw that knowledge about another world of thought, about things which do not exist in the usual sense of the word, can be used in everyday life to answer questions about the real world. Is this not surprising?

HIPPOCRATES More than that, it is incomprehensible. It is really a miracle.

SOCRATES Perhaps it is not so mysterious at all, and if we open the shell of this question, we may find a real pearl.

HIPPOCRATES Please, my dear Socrates, do not speak in puzzles like the Pythia.

SOCRATES Tell me then, are you surprised when somebody who has travelled in distant countries, who has seen and experienced many things, returns to his city and uses his experience to give good advice to his fellow citizens?

HIPPOCRATES Not at all.

SOCRATES Even if the countries which the traveller has visited are very far away and are inhabited by quite a different sort of people, speaking another language, worshipping other gods?

HIPPOCRATES Not even in that case, because there is much that is common between different people.

SOCRATES Now tell me, if it turned out that the world of mathematics is, in spite of its peculiarities, in some sense similar to our real world, would you still find it miraculous that mathematics can be applied to the study of the real world?

HIPPOCRATES   In that case no, but I do not see any similarity between the real world and the imaginary world of mathematics.

SOCRATES   Do you see that rock on the other side of the river, there where the river broadens out and forms a lake?

HIPPOCRATES   I see it.

SOCRATES   And do you see the image of the rock reflected in the water?

HIPPOCRATES   Certainly I do.

SOCRATES   Then tell me, what is the difference between the rock and its reflection?

HIPPOCRATES   The rock is a solid piece of hard matter. It is made warm by the sun. If you touched it, you would feel that it is rough. The reflected image cannot be touched; if I put my hand on it, I would touch only the cool water. As a matter of fact, the reflected image does not really exist; it is illusion, nothing else.

SOCRATES   Is there nothing in common between the rock and its reflected image?

HIPPOCRATES   Well, in a certain sense, the reflected image is a faithful picture of the rock. The contour of the rock, even its small abutments, are clearly visible in the reflected image. But what of it? Do you want to say that the world of mathematics is a reflected image of the real world in the mirror of our thinking?

SOCRATES   You said it, and very well.

HIPPOCRATES   But how is that possible?

SOCRATES   Let us recall how the abstract concepts of mathematics developed. We said that the mathematician deals with pure numbers, and not with the numbers of real objects. But do you think that somebody who has never counted real objects can understand the abstract notion of number? When a child learns counting, he first counts pebbles and small sticks. Only if he knows that two pebbles and three pebbles make five pebbles, and the same about sticks or coins, is he able to understand that two and three make five. The situation is essentially the same with geometry. The child arrives at the notion of a sphere through experiences with round objects like balls. Mankind developed all fundamental notions of mathematics in a similar way. These notions are crystallized from a knowledge of the real world, and thus it is not surprising but quite natural that they bear the marks of their origin, as children do of their parents. And exactly as children when they grow up become the supporters of their parents, so any branch of mathematics, if it is sufficiently developed, becomes a useful tool in exploring the real world.

HIPPOCRATES Now it is quite clear to me how a knowledge of the non-existent things of the world of mathematics can be used in everyday life. You rendered me a great service in helping me to understand this.

SOCRATES I envy you, my dear Hippocrates, because I still wonder about one thing which I should like to have settled. Perhaps you can help me.

HIPPOCRATES I would do so with pleasure, but I am afraid you are mocking me again. Do not make me ashamed by asking my help, but tell me frankly the question which I overlooked.

SOCRATES You will see it yourself if you try to summarize the results of our discussion.

HIPPOCRATES Well, when it became clear why mathematics is able to give certain knowledge about a world different from the world in which we live, about the world of human thought, the question remained as to the use of this knowledge. Now we have found that the world of mathematics is nothing else but a reflection in our mind of the real world. This makes it clear that every discovery about the world of mathematics gives us some information about the real world. I am completely satisfied with this answer.

SOCRATES   If I tell you the answer is not yet complete, I do so not because I want to confuse you, but because I am sure that sooner or later you will raise the question yourself and will reproach me for not having called your attention to it. You would say: "Tell me, Socrates, what is the sense of studying the reflected image if we can study the object itself?"

HIPPOCRATES   You are perfectly right; it is an obvious question. You are a wizard, Socrates. You can totally confuse me by a few words, and you can knock down by an innocent-looking question the whole edifice which we have built with so much trouble. I should, of course, answer that if we are able to have a look at the original thing, it makes no sense to look at the reflected image. But I am sure this shows only that our simile fails at this point. Certainly there is an answer, only I do not know how to find it.

SOCRATES   Your guess is correct that the paradox arose because we kept too close to the simile of the reflected image. A simile is like a bow—if you stretch it too far, it snaps. Let us drop it and choose another one. You certainly know that travellers and sailors make good use of maps.

HIPPOCRATES   I have experienced that myself. Do you mean that mathematics furnishes a map of the real world?

SOCRATES   Yes. Can you now answer the question: what advantage would it be to look at the map instead of looking at the landscape?

HIPPOCRATES This is clear: using the map we can scan vast distances which could be covered only by travelling many weeks or months. The map shows us not every detail, but only the most important things. Therefore it is useful if we want to plan a long voyage.

SOCRATES Very well. But there is something else which occurred to me.

HIPPOCRATES What is it?

SOCRATES There is another reason why the study of the mathematical image of the world may be of use. If mathematicians discover some property of the circle, this at once gives us some information about any object of circular shape. Thus, the method of mathematics enables us to deal with different things at the same time.

HIPPOCRATES What about the following similes: If somebody looks at a city from the top of a nearby mountain, he gets a more comprehensive view than if he walks through its crooked streets; or if a general watches the movements of an enemy army from a hill, he gets a clearer picture of the situation than does the soldier in the front line who sees only those directly opposite him.

SOCRATES Well, you surpass me in inventing new similes, but as I do not want to fall behind, let me also add one parable. Recently I looked at a painting by Aristophon, the son of Aglaophon, and the painter warned me, "If you go too near the picture, Socrates, you will see only colored spots, but you will not see the whole picture."

HIPPOCRATES Of course, he was right, and so were you, when you did not let us finish our discussion before we got to the heart of the question. But I think it is time for us to return to the city because the shadows of night are falling and I am hungry and thirsty. If you still have some patience, I would like to ask you something while we walk.

SOCRATES All right, let us start and you may ask your question.

HIPPOCRATES Our discourse convinced me fully that I should start studying mathematics and I am very grateful to you for this. But tell me, why are you yourself not doing mathematics? Judging from your deep understanding of the real nature and importance of mathematics, it is my guess that you would sur-pass all other mathematicians of Hellas, were you to concentrate on it. I would be glad to follow you as your pupil in mathematics if you accepted me.

SOCRATES No, my dear Hippocrates, this is not my business. Theodoros knows much more about mathematics than I do and you cannot find a better master than him. As to your question of why I myself am not a mathematician, I shall give you the rea-sons. I do not conceal my high opinion about mathematics. I think that we Hellenes have in no other art made such important progress as in mathematics, and this is only the beginning. If we do not extinguish each other in mad wars, we shall obtain won-derful results as discoverers as well as inventors. You asked me why I do not join the ranks of those who develop this great sci-ence. As a matter of fact, I am some sort of a mathematician, only of a different kind. An inner voice, you may call it an oracle, to which I always listen carefully, asked me many years ago, "What is the source of the great advances which the mathematicians have made in their noble science?" I answered, "I think the source of the success of mathematicians lies in their methods, the high standards of their logic, their striving without the least compromise to the full truth, their habit of starting always from first principles, of defining every notion used exactly and of avoiding self-contradictions." My inner voice answered, "Very well, but why do you think, Socrates, that this method of thinking and arguing can be used only for the study of numbers and geometric forms? Why do you not try to convince your fellow citizens to apply the same high logical standards in every other field, for instance in philosophy and politics, in discussing the problems of everyday private and public life?" From that time on, this has been my goal. *I have demonstrated* (you remember, for instance, our discussion with Protagoras) *that those who are thought to be wise men are mostly ignorant fools. All their arguing lacks solid foundation, since they use*—contrary to mathematicians—*undefined and only half-understood notions.* By this activity I have succeeded in making almost everybody my enemy. This is not surprising because for all people who are sluggish in thinking and idly content to use obscure terms, I am a living reproach. People do not like those who constantly remind them of the faults which they are unable or unwilling to correct. The day will come when these people will fall upon me and exterminate me. But until that day comes, I shall continue to follow my calling. You, however, go to Theodoros.

A DIALOGUE ON
THE APPLICATIONS OF
MATHEMATICS

ARCHIMEDES

A DIALOGUE ON THE APPLICATIONS
OF MATHEMATICS

ARCHIMEDES   Your Majesty! What a surprise at this late hour! To what do I owe the honor of a visit from King Hieron to my modest home?

HIERON   My dear friend Archimedes, this evening we had a dinner in my palace to celebrate the great triumph of our small city, Syracuse, over the mighty Romans. I invited you, but your place remained empty. Why didn't you come, you to whom above all we owe today's victory? Your huge, concave brazen mirrors set afire ten of the twenty big ships of the Romans; they sped like fiery torches out of the harbor in the southwest gale; all went down before reaching the open sea. I could not go to sleep without thanking you for delivering our city from the enemy.

ARCHIMEDES   They may come back, and we are still surrounded on the mainland.

HIERON   We shall speak about that later. First let me hand you a present, the best I can give.

ARCHIMEDES   A wonderful masterpiece indeed!

HIERON This tray is of pure gold; you may test it with your method, you will find no trace of silver in it.

ARCHIMEDES The reliefs show the adventures of Odysseus, I assume. In the middle I see the unsuspecting Trojans pulling the giant wooden horse into their city—I always wondered whether the Trojans used some sort of compound pulley to accomplish that. Of course, the horse stood on wheels, but the road to the city must have been rather steep.

HIERON My dear Achimedes, by Zeus, forget your pulleys for a moment. You know how astonished I was when by yourself you launched the heavy ship I wanted to send to King Ptolemy, simply by turning the handle of your triple pulley. But have a look at the other scenes on the tray.

ARCHIMEDES I recognize the Cyclops, and Circe as she changes the companions of Odysseus into pigs, and here the concert of Sirens to which Odysseus listens while he is chained to the mast of his ship (if you look at his face you can almost hear the enticing song). And there is Odysseus in the netherworld, meeting the shadow of Achilles, and here he is frightening the charming Nausicaä and her girls, and finally, of course, the scene where Odysseus, disguised as an old beggar, spans his bow and squares his account with the suitors—a marvelous piece of art. I thank you, my gracious king; this is truly a king's gift.

HIERON It was the best piece in my treasure-house, but you deserve it. I chose it not only for its beauty and value, but for a third reason. What you did today for Syracuse can be compared only with the trick of Odysseus. Both are triumphs of a sharp mind over brute force.

ARCHIMEDES You make an old man blush. But let me remind you again that the war is not over yet. Would you like to hear the advice of an old man?

HIERON   I even order you, as your king, to tell me your opinion frankly.

ARCHIMEDES   This is the moment when you should make peace with the Romans; since the war began, we have never been in such a favorable bargaining position. If Marcellus does not send his envoy to you before midnight, you should send yours to him before dawn, and make peace before the sun sets again. Marcellus is eager to withdraw the troops which besiege the city because he needs to use them against Hannibal. Moreover, if he can reach an agreement tomorrow, he can report to Rome a victory, if only a diplomatic one, and not just the sad news that half his fleet is lost. When the report about today's battle reaches Rome, the Romans will be so furious that they will not be satisfied with anything less than total victory.

HIERON   Your analysis is correct. As a matter of fact, I received a message from Marcellus this evening in which he offered peace and withdrawal of his troops under certain conditions. If you knew these conditions, you would be less keen on making a deal with the Romans.

ARCHIMEDES   What does Marcellus want?

HIERON   Well, of course he wants a lot of gold and silver. He also wants ten new ships for the ten we sank today, and further that all our forts be demolished except one in which a garrison of Roman soldiers would be stationed. He wants us to declare war on Carthage, and finally he demands my son Gelon, my daughter Helena, and you as hostages. He promises, however, that no harm will be done to the city and its inhabitants as long as we adhere to the treaty.

ARCHIMEDES   Perhaps he will not insist on everything, although he will insist that you hand me over to him.

HIERON   You speak coolly about this. By all the gods of Olympus, as long as I am alive I will not place my children in the hands of the enemy, nor will I give you to them. I do not mind the gold and the ships, he can have them. But what I dislike most about his conditions is that if we fulfill them, we shall be completely at his mercy. What guarantees are there that he will keep the treaty? He does not give me any hostages.

ARCHIMEDES   Take care not to question whether he will stick to his word; Romans are sensitive about their honor, at least during negotiations. But perhaps you can avoid giving him your children.

HIERON   And what about you? Would you be ready to make this sacrifice for your city?

ARCHIMEDES   Is that a question or a request?

HIERON   A question only, of course. Do you want to know what I replied to Marcellus?

ARCHIMEDES   You have answered already?

HIERON   Yes. I accepted all his conditions except that of giving you as a hostage; but I agreed to give my children as hostages only under the condition that he send me two of his children as hostages. As for you, I told him that your age does not permit your living in camp. However, knowing that he does not really want you as a hostage but only wants your wisdom, I promised that you would write him a full description of all your inventions which are of military importance.

ARCHIMEDES   I will never write anything about my inventions concerning warfare.

HIERON   Why not? If there is peace, we will not need them any more. Explain why you refuse to write about your inventions.

ARCHIMEDES   If you have the patience to listen to my reasons, I shall do so.

HIERON   I am ready to listen. I want to remain awake and wait for Marcellus' answer.

ARCHIMEDES   Then we have a lot of time because it will take Marcellus awhile to formulate his answer. It will sound like a whip.

HIERON   Do you think he will discontinue the negotiations?

ARCHIMEDES   Of course. You contested his honor. He will never forgive that, and there will be no agreement.

HIERON   You may be right.

ARCHIMEDES   I have always admired your artful diplomacy and your psychological insight into your opponents' hearts. But this time you neglected this art.

HIERON   I have to admit it. Perhaps I was too drunk with wine and victory. But what is done is done. Still, I want to hear your reasons.

ARCHIMEDES   Though the question becomes an academic one, nevertheless, I shall explain my point of view. You compared my machines with the wooden horse of Troy. Well, your comparison is really very close, but in quite a different sense. Odysseus used the wooden horse to smuggle himself and some Greek soldiers into Troy. I used my machines to smuggle an idea into the public mind of the Greek world, the idea being that mathematics—not only its elements, but also its most subtle parts—can be applied successfully to practical purposes. I must confess that I hesitated quite a lot before doing this because I hate war and murder. But the war was here anyway, and this was the only way to make myself understood. I have tried other ways, but in vain. May I remind you that some years ago when I invented a pump to take the water out of your mines so that the people who work there should not wade to their hips in it, you were not interested. The supervisor of your mines told me he did not

33

care about the legs of slaves getting wet—they were not made of salt; these were his words. And do you remember when I proposed to make a machine to irrigate your fields? I was told that slave work was cheaper. And when I proposed to use the force of steam to drive the mills of King Ptolemy, what was his answer? He said that the mills which served his ancestors would serve him as well. Shall I remind you of other examples? There were at least a dozen others. All my endeavors to show the world what mathematics can do for them in peace were in vain. But as war approached, suddenly you remembered my pulleys, cog-wheels and levers. In peacetime everybody regarded my inventions as toys, unworthy of a serious grown-up citizen, still less of a philosopher. Even you, who always supported me and helped me to realize my ideas, did not take them quite seriously; you showed them to your guests to entertain them, but that was all. Then the war came and the Roman ships closed the harbor; I ventured a casual remark, that by throwing stones on them with a catapult we could drive them away; you jumped at the idea. I could not take back what I had said, and had to go ahead. Once I started on this road, I had to continue. But my feelings about it were mixed from the start. I was, of course, happy that my inventions were not ridiculed anymore, and that at last I had a chance to show the world what mathematics in action really was. But this was not the sort of action by which I wanted to prove the practical value of mathematical ideas. I saw men killed by my machines and this made me feel guilty. I made a solemn oath to Athena that I would never tell the secret of my war machines to anybody either by word or in writing. I tried to soothe my conscience by telling myself that the news about Archimedes defeating the Romans by mathematics would reach all corners of the Greek-speaking world, and this would be remembered even when the war was over and the secrets of my war-machines were buried with me.

HIERON It is true, my dear Archimedes; I am getting letters from kings who are my friends asking about your inventions.

ARCHIMEDES And what do you answer them?

HIERON I tell them that these questions cannot be answered as long as the war continues.

ARCHIMEDES I hope you understand now what my reasons are for not publicizing my secrets. I succeeded in keeping them even from those who carry out my plans. Each man knows about some detail only. I am glad you never asked me questions because I would have refused to answer.

HIERON But now I shall ask you some questions. Don't be afraid, I shall not ask for your secrets, only about the underlying general principles.

ARCHIMEDES I think I can answer such questions without breaking my oath.

HIERON Before I begin, I want to ask you something else. Why was it so important to you that your ideas about the usefulness of mathematics be accepted?

ARCHIMEDES Perhaps I was a fool, but I thought that I could change the course of history. I was worried about the future of our Greek world. I thought that if we applied mathematics on a large scale—after all, mathematics is a Greek invention, and I think the best achievement of the Greek spirit—we might save our Greek way of life. Now I realize that it is too late. The Romans will conquer not only Syracuse but all other Greek cities too; our time is over.

HIERON Even were that the case, our Greek culture would not be lost: the Romans would take it over. Look how they try to imitate us already. They copy our statues, translate our literature —and you see that Marcellus is already interested in your mathematics.

ARCHIMEDES   The Romans will never really understand it. They are too practical-minded, and they are not interested in abstract ideas.

HIERON   They are certainly interested in its practical uses.

ARCHIMEDES   But these things cannot be separated. One has to be a dreamer of dreams to apply mathematics with real success.

HIERON   That sounds rather paradoxical. I thought that to apply mathematics one should first of all have a good practical sense. This leads me to my first question. What really is the secret of the new science which you invented—let us call it applied mathematics? And what is the main difference between your applied mathematics and that sort of mathematics—let us call it pure mathematics—which is taught in the schools?

ARCHIMEDES   I am sorry to disappoint you. There exists no other kind of mathematics besides that which your teachers taught you, and not without success, as I recall. Applied mathematics, as an art which is different and separated from mathematics as such, does not exist! My secret is so well hidden because it is no secret at all; its very obviousness is its best disguise. It is hidden like a golden coin thrown into the dust of the street.

HIERON   Do you mean that your marvelous machines are based on the sort of mathematics every educated man knows?

ARCHIMEDES   You are getting nearer the truth.

HIERON   Could you give me an example?

ARCHIMEDES   Well, let us take as an example the mirrors which did such a good job today. What I did was simply to remember a well-known property of the parabola: take any point P of a parabola, connect it with the focus, and draw through P a line which is parallel to the axis. These two lines form equal angles with the tangent to the parabola in the point P. You can find this theorem in the books of my distinguished colleagues of Alexandria.

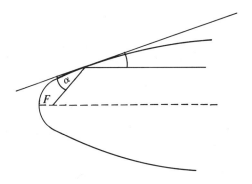

HIERON   It is hard to believe you have destroyed half the fleet of Marcellus by this theorem, which is one of hundreds of similar geometrical propositions. I remember it vaguely, though I forget its proof.

ARCHIMEDES   Probably when you heard one of its ingenious proofs you understood it, and perhaps even admired its beauty and elegance, but that was all. Some mathematicians went one step further; they explored some of its purely geometrical consequences, or invented new proofs, but there they stopped. I simply went just one step further; I looked at its non-mathematical consequences also.

HIERON   I thought you invented some new law of optics.

ARCHIMEDES   Optics is, after all, nothing but another branch of geometry. What I used from optics, the law of reflection of a ray, has also been known a long time.

HIERON   Do you mean that in order to apply mathematics one does not need to get new mathematical results, only to fit together a practical situation and its mathematical counterpart, some well-known mathematical proposition?

ARCHIMEDES No, it is not quite so simple. It often happens that the theorem which one needs does not exist, and one has to find and prove it oneself. But even if this is not necessary, to find the mathematical counterpart—as you call it (I prefer to call it a mathematical model)—of a practical situation is not the same as matching gloves. First of all, one can construct many mathematical models for the same practical situation, and one has to choose the most appropriate, that which fits the situation as closely as practical aims require (it can never fit completely). At the same time, it must not be too complicated, but still must be mathematically feasible. These are, of course, conflicting requirements and a delicate balancing of the two is usually necessary. You have to approximate closely the real situation in every respect important for your purposes, but lay aside everything which is of no importance for your actual aims. A model need not to be similar to the modeled reality in every respect, only in those which really count. On the other hand, the same mathematical model can be used to fit quite different practical situations. For instance, I also used the properties of parabolas to construct catapults, because the track of a stone thrown by a catapult can be approximated to some extent by a parabola. I also used parabolas to compute how deep a ship will dip into the sea under the weight of its load. Of course, the cross section of a ship has not exactly the same shape as a parabola, but a more realistic model would not have been mathematically manageable. The results were, nevertheless, in fairly good agreement with the facts. Especially I was able to find out under what conditions a ship would be able to stand upright when buffeted by the wind and the waves, because its center of gravity tends to be in the deepest possible position. In trying to describe such a complicated situation, even a very rough model may be useful because it gives at least qualitatively correct results, and these may be of even greater practical importance than quantitative results. My experience has taught me that even a crude mathematical model can help us to understand a practical situation better, because in trying to set up a mathematical model we are forced to think over all logical possibilities, to define all notions unambiguously, and to distinguish between important and secondary factors. Even if a mathematical model leads to results which are not in accordance with the facts, it may be useful because the failure of one model can help us find a better one.

HIERON   It seems to me that applied mathematics is similar to warfare: sometimes a defeat is more valuable than a victory because it helps us to realize the inadequacy of our arms or of our strategy.

ARCHIMEDES   Now you have really grasped the essential point.

HIERON   Tell me something more about your mirrors.

ARCHIMEDES   I have told you the basic idea already. After I hit on the idea of using the mentioned property of parabolas, I had to solve the question of how to grind and polish a metal mirror into the form of a concave paraboloid of revolution, but I would prefer not to speak about this. Of course, I also had to select an appropriate alloy.

HIERON   Without intruding into your secrets—it is clear that besides the properties of the parabola you also had to know a lot about metals and the art of dealing with them. This shows, it seems to me, that the knowledge of mathematics is not sufficient if somebody wants to apply it. Isn't a man who wants to apply mathematics in a position similar to that of a man who wants to ride two horses at the same time?

ARCHIMEDES   I would change your simile slightly: he who wants to apply mathematics is like a man who wants to harness two horses to his carriage. This is not so difficult to do. Some knowledge of the horses as well as of the carriage is, of course, needed, but any of your coachmen has such knowledge.

HIERON Now I am quite confused: every time I think that applied mathematics is mysterious, you show me that it is really quite simple; but when I become convinced that the whole thing is really simple, you point out that it is much more complicated than I imagined.

ARCHIMEDES Its principles are obvious, but the details are sometimes quite involved.

HIERON I do not understand yet what you mean by a mathematical model. Tell me more about this.

ARCHIMEDES   Do you remember the sphere I constructed some years ago to imitate the motions of the sun, the moon and the five planets, the one by which it was possible to show how the eclipses of the sun and the moon happen?

HIERON   Of course, it is one of the things in the palace that I show to all my visitors; everybody thinks that it is marvelous. Is this a mathematical model of the universe?

ARCHIMEDES   No, I would call it a physical model. Mathematical models are invisible, they exist only in our mind, and can be expressed only by formulae. A mathematical model of the universe is that which is common to the real universe and to my physical model. In the physical model, for instance, each planet is a tiny ball about the size of an orange. In my mathematical model of the universe the planets are represented simply by points.

HIERON   I think I am beginning to understand what you mean by a mathematical model. But let us return to the simile about horses. The art of harnessing horses to a carriage and driving them is quite different from that of breeding and raising them. Isn't the art of applying mathematics quite distinct from that of finding and proving theorems?

ARCHIMEDES   You are, of course, right about horses, though the man who has raised a horse usually knows the most about it and can drive it better than anybody else. As regards mathematics, I pointed out earlier that in order to be able to apply it successfully one has to have a deep understanding of it, and if somebody wants to apply mathematics in an original way, he has to be a creative mathematician. Conversely, a concern with applications can aid in pure mathematical research.

HIERON   How is that possible? Could you give an example?

ARCHIMEDES   Perhaps you remember that some time ago I was very interested in a question of mechanics, namely in finding the center of gravity of a body. The results which I obtained about centers of gravity helped me to build machines, and also they helped me to prove new geometrical propositions. *I have developed a peculiar method which consists of investigating geometrical problems by means of mechanical considerations concerning centers of gravity. This method is of a heuristic character; this means it does not furnish exact proofs. Many theorems first became clear to me by using this method of reasoning. Of course, as the method does not furnish actual demonstrations, I afterwards proved the theorems I conjectured by means of my mechanical method by the traditional methods of geometry. It is much easier to supply the proof if one has previously acquired some knowledge of the question through mechanical analogies, and thus knows what must be proved.*

HIERON   Tell me one theorem which you have found in this strange way.

ARCHIMEDES   *The area of any segment of a parabola is four–thirds the area of the triangle which has the same base and height.* After finding the result with my method, I found a proof along traditional lines too.

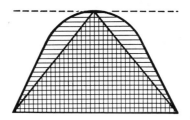

HIERON   If you found this theorem by mechanics, why did you bother about the geometrical proof?

ARCHIMEDES   When I first discovered my method, the results which I got with its help were not all correct; later, by analyzing the cases in which the method misled me, I developed it so far that now it never misleads me. But still I cannot prove that every result I get this way is really true; maybe somebody will prove this some day, but until that time I do not have complete confidence in the method.

HIERON   But are strict proofs in applied mathematics really necessary? After all, as you said, the mathematical model is only an approximation of reality. If you use approximately correct formulae, your results will be still approximately close to reality and they can never be absolutely correct anyway.

ARCHIMEDES   You are mistaken, my king. Just because the mathematical model is only an approximation and there is always a certain discrepancy with the facts, one has to take care not to increase this discrepancy further by a careless use of mathematics. One has to be as accurate as possible. By the way, in regard to approximations, there is a common misunderstanding that using approximations means departing from mathematical precision. Approximations have a precise theory, and results about approximations—for instance, inequalities—have to be proved as rigorously as identities. Perhaps you remember the approximations which I gave for the area of a circle with given diameter; I proved them with a rigor usual in geometry.

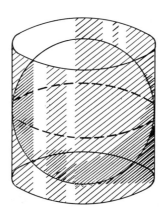

HIERON   What other results did you find by your mechanical method?

ARCHIMEDES   This method also led me to discover that *the volume of a sphere is two–thirds the volume of a circumscribed cylinder.*

HIERON   I heard you say that when you die, you want this theorem to be inscribed on your gravestone. Does it mean that you consider this your most outstanding conclusion?

ARCHIMEDES   I think the method itself is more important than any of the particular results I got with its help. Do you remember when I told you once, speaking about levers: *"Give me a place to stand and I can move the earth"?* Of course, there exists no such fixed point in the world. However, in mathematics, one does have such a fixed point to lean on, namely, axioms and logic. To apply mathematics to problems of the real world means to move the earth from the fixed point of mathematics.

HIERON   You always speak about applying mathematics, but all the examples you give are applications of geometry. In regard to geometry, I now see how it can be applied. For instance, the functioning of a machine depends on the form and size of its components; the track of a stone thrown by your catapult is a curve, approximately a parabola, as you said. But what about other branches of mathematics, say number theory? I can hardly imagine how it can have any practical importance. Of course, I am not speaking about the elements of arithmetic which are clearly used in every sort of computation; I mean things like divisibility, prime numbers, least common multiple and other similar topics.

ARCHIMEDES   Well, if you connect two cogwheels each with a different number of teeth, the least common multiple comes in inevitably. Does this simple example convince you? Recently I got a letter from my friend Eratosthenes of Cyrene in which he wrote about a simple but ingenious method—he calls it the sieve method—which he invented to find prime numbers. Thinking about his method, I made a sketch of a machine which realizes his idea. This machine works with a set of cogwheels: when you turn it a number of times, say *n,* and look into a hole, if the view is clear, the number *n* is prime; but if the view is closed, then *n* is composite.

HIERON   That is really amazing. When the war is over, you must build this machine. My guests will love it.

ARCHIMEDES   If I am alive, I shall certainly do so. It will show that machines can solve mathematical problems. Perhaps it will help mathematicians to realize that, even from their own point of view, they may gain something from studying the relation of mathematics and machines.

HIERON   Speaking about gains, I recall a story about Euclid. *One of his students studying geometry asked Euclid, "What shall I gain by learning these things?" Whereupon Euclid called his slave and said, "Give him a coin, since he wants to gain from what he learns."* It seems to me that this story shows Euclid thought it unnecessary for a mathematician to bother about the practical use of his results.

ARCHIMEDES   I have, of course, heard the anecdote, but you will be surprised when I tell you that I sympathize completely with Euclid. In his place I would have said something similar.

HIERON   Now I am confused again. Up to now you spoke enthusiastically about the applications of mathematics, and now you agree with the purists who think that the only reward which a scientist should expect is the pleasure of knowledge.

ARCHIMEDES   I think you and most people misunderstand the story about Euclid. It does not mean that he was not interested in the practical consequences of mathematical results and that he considered them unworthy of a philosopher. This is pure nonsense; he has written, as you certainly know, a book called *Phaenomena*, about astronomy, and a book on optics, and he is probably the author of the book *Catoptrica* too, which I used in constructing my mirrors; he was also interested in mechanics. As I understand the story, Euclid wanted to emphasize the remarkable fact that mathematics rewards only those who are interested in it not only because of its rewards but also because of itself. Mathematics is like your daughter, Helena, who suspects every time a suitor appears that he is not really in love with her, but is interested in her only because he wants to be the son-in-law of the king. She wants a husband who loves her for her own beauty, her wit and charm, and not for the wealth and power which he can get by marrying her. Similarly, mathematics reveals its secrets only to those who approach it with pure love, for its own beauty. Those who do this are, of course, also rewarded with results of practical importance. But if somebody asks at each step, "What can I profit by this?" he will not get far. You remember I told you that the Romans would never be really successful in applying mathematics. Well, now you see why; they are too practical-minded.

HIERON   I think we should learn from the Romans, then we would have better chances in fighting them.

ARCHIMEDES   I do not agree. If we try to win by giving up the ideas we stand for and by imitating our opponents, we are lost before the battle begins. Even if we could win the war in this way, it would not be worthwhile; such a victory is worse than a defeat.

HIERON   Let us not speak about the war but return the mathematics. Tell me, how do you construct your mathematical models?

ARCHIMEDES   It is difficult to explain this in general terms. Perhaps a simile will help. A mathematical model of a real situation is something like its shadow on the screen of the mind.

HIERON   It seems to me that your philosophy is the exact opposite of Plato's. He says that real things are the shadows of ideas, while if I correctly understood the meaning of your words, you are saying that ideas are the shadows of reality.

ARCHIMEDES   The two points of view are not so far from each other as it seems. Plato was puzzled by the correspondence between mathematical ideas and reality, and he thought that the main task of philosophy was to explain this correspondence. Up to that point, I agree with him completely. I do not agree with his explanation, but at least he saw the problem clearly and tried to work out one of the logically possible answers. But I think we have to leave philosophy and return to the facts of life— I hear somebody knocking at the door. I shall open it.

HIERON   Let me do it. It must be my envoy with Marcellus' answer. Here is the message.

ARCHIMEDES   What is his answer?

HIERON   Read it yourself.

ARCHIMEDES   Let me see. "Marcellus sends his greetings to King Hieron and announces that he will conquer Syracuse before the new moon; then King Hieron will realize that a Roman keeps his word."

HIERON   Now what do you think about that?

ARCHIMEDES   His Greek is really not bad. As for the contents, they are what I expected.

HIERON   Truly, your prediction was as correct as if you had found it by your method.

ARCHIMEDES   Well, at least we know now what to expect.

HIERON   I must go, I need some sleep. Tomorrow we have to prepare ourselves for a new attack. Thank you for this interesting talk.

ARCHIMEDES   I enjoyed it very much. I don't often have the opportunity to talk about mathematics nowadays. Thank you again for the wonderful tray.

HIERON   I am glad you like it. Good night, my friend. I think you need rest too.

ARCHIMEDES   Good night, my king. I will not sleep yet. I want to finish a letter to my friend Dositheus of Pelusium about my latest results. Now that the Roman fleet is gone, there will certainly be ships leaving the harbor tomorrow, but perhaps after tomorrow the Romans will set up the blockade again. I want to use this opportunity; it may be the last one.

A DIALOGUE ON
THE LANGUAGE OF
THE BOOK OF NATURE

GALILEO

A DIALOGUE ON THE LANGUAGE OF
THE BOOK OF NATURE

TORRICELLI   Allow me, Madame, to introduce myself. I am Evangelista Torricelli, a student of Abbot Castelli.

MRS. NICCOLINI   Ah, so you are the young man who wrote that enthusiastic letter in which you call yourself a Copernican and Galileist?

TORRICELLI   Many of us young people think that way. I heard from Abbot Castelli about the new work which the Master has started to write, and I would like to speak to him about it.

MRS. NICCOLINI   Don't you know that Galileo is the prisoner of the Holy Court of Justice? They allow him to live here in the house of my husband, contrary to what is usual, only because the Grand Duke of Tuscany emphatically requested it. My husband who is the Grand Duke's ambassador, had to promise not to allow Galileo any visitors.

TORRICELLI   No one knows I have come; I was unobserved.

MRS. NICCOLINI   All right, but only because I think the old man will be pleased to talk with someone who understands his ideas. For want of other listeners, he sometimes talks to me about his new work; but often I cannot follow him. Today he is in good spirits because he slept well last night—after many sleepless weeks. Come with me. If somebody happens to see you, we shall say that you are a relative of mine and have come to visit.

TORRICELLI Thank you, Signora, you do me great honor.

MRS. NICCOLINI Come this way please . . . Signor Galileo, I have brought a guest you will be glad to meet, Evangelista Torricelli.

GALILEO Of course, I am delighted. How admirable that you are not afraid to visit an old man suspected of heresy.

TORRICELLI My friends and I regard your dialogue about the two great cosmic systems as our bible. I heard from Abbot Castelli that you are now working on a new book which will surpass everything that was ever written about mechanics. I have come to hear something about it.

GALILEO For a long time I had planned to write this book. Some months ago I started it at last, but my work was interrupted because I was summoned to the Inquisition here in Rome. Since then, I have not had the time to write even a line. However, I desire nothing more than to finish this work wherein I summarize all my knowledge about motion. It will certainly surpass all my previous works. But I am very much afraid that I will not be able to complete it. Even were I to come victorious from this fight—into which I was forced—it would be a Pyrrhic victory should I not have the strength to finish my book.

TORRICELLI I would very much like to hear something about its contents.

GALILEO The Greek mathematicians attained amazing results in their work, and some of them—for example, Archimedes—applied their results to different practical questions with magnificent success. But they shrank from the mathematical study of motion and since that time nobody has attempted it. In my work, if it is ever finished, the most essential part will be the mathematical description of motion.

TORRICELLI   It is really incomprehensible why the Greeks did not try to do this. What could have been the cause of it?

GALILEO   The Greek philosophers frequently discussed motion. Take, for example, the paradoxes of Zeno about Achilles and the turtle, and about the arrow; by these he attempted to show that motion is impossible. Zeno really wanted to say that the concept of motion is contradictory and, therefore, motion cannot be treated by mathematical methods. Aristotle tried to disprove the paradoxes of Zeno, but this rebuttal proved only what every child knows: namely, that there is motion. The real confutation of Zeno's paradoxes would be a demonstration that motion can be described by mathematics. This Aristotle did not even try. My work, if it is ever finished, will be the first actual confutation of the paradoxes of Zeno. As a matter of fact, Aristotle and Zeno both said that the study of motion cannot be the task of mathematics. However, Aristotle's motivation in asserting that was different from Zeno's. According to Aristotle, the natural sciences deal with independently existing but changeable things, while mathematics deals with unchangeable but not independently existing things; and the dependently existing and changing things— motion being among them—cannot be the topic of any science. Thus, for almost 2000 years, Aristotle's veto discouraged mathematicians and philosophers from the mathematical study of motion. His false teaching erected an unnatural barrier between mathematics and the natural sciences, one which only a few people dared to transgress.

TORRICELLI   I am looking forward to reading your work. What a shame, Master, that you are molested with ridiculous charges that prevent you from writing this book which will open a new age in science! But allow me to ask one question: why did you come to Rome instead of staying in some place where you would not be disturbed in your efforts?

GALILEO What could I do? The Inquisition summoned me.

TORRICELLI You could have escaped to a place where the hand of the Inquisition could not reach you.

GALILEO *When I came to Rome, I still hoped that I should be able to convince the Church that the question of the motion of the earth is not a question of faith, but a question of fact, the discussion of which should be left to science.* I felt that I was obliged—not only to science but even to the Church—to explain this. If the Church continues to support the Ptolemaic system, it will be in the same position as someone who remains on board a sinking ship. I tried to show this with my dialogue, and I thought if the opportunity to give my arguments in person presented itself, I could persuade the Church to change her opinion of the Copernican theory. *I was sure that I could convince the Pope, whom I knew in the old days when he was only Cardinal Maffeo Barberini, to side with me. He gave many signs of honoring and esteeming me—perhaps you heard that once he even wrote a poem to me. And I always knew him to be a friend of science.* For instance he began his functions as Pope by releasing from prison the unfortunate Campanella. I thought if I had a chance to speak with him, I could convince him that it was in the interest of the Church to allow science a free hand to study the question of the earth's motion. But in that hope I was disappointed; the Pope does not even want to hear about me. My enemies made him believe that in my dialogue I sought to make him ridiculous through the character of the stupid Simplicio; and now the old friendship has changed to hate and vengefulness. Perhaps you are right that I should not have come to Rome, but now it is too late to sorrow about it.

TORRICELLI I don't think it is too late. May I speak openly?

GALILEO From Signora Niccolini I keep no secrets; I have no better friend. She induced her uncle, Pater Riccardi, to permit the publication of my dialogue. Now that I live here, she takes care of me like a mother, and she is always thinking about how she can console me, how she can strengthen me to endure these trials I have to suffer with my grey head. Before her, you can speak frankly.

TORRICELLI I had no doubts about that; when Signora Niccolini allowed me to visit you I understood that I could trust her. But nowadays even the walls have ears.

MRS. NICCOLINI In this house you can speak safely.

GALILEO You can believe this, my young friend. Just a few days ago, Signora Niccolini dismissed one of her servants because it turned out that he spied for the Inquisition; but she did not tell me so because she did not want to upset me. Isn't that so, Catherine?

MRS. NICCOLINI Well, since you have found out anyway, I admit it. But I trust my other servants; they are all Florentines and reliable men. You may speak openly; what you say will be our secret.

TORRICELLI My friends and I, who call ourselves Galileists, have prepared everything for your escape. First we would take you to Venice; there you would be safe from the Inquisition for awhile because the Republic could not extradite you under any circumstances. If you wanted to, you could then go from there, by ship, to the Netherlands where you could work quite undisturbed and where your new book could be printed. We have considered all the details. If you say yes, we can agree immediately on the date.

GALILEO My hosts are responsible for me and I do not want to cause trouble for them. Apart from everything else, this alone is reason enough why I cannot accept your proposal.

TORRICELLI   We considered that too. It is our plan to seize you from the hands of the Inquisition the next time you are being conducted to the Holy Office for an audience. It will happen on the street, and so nobody will be able to blame Signor Ambassador Niccolini. We have some reliable men who could easily deal with the guards.

GALILEO   I cannot tell you how happy it makes me to know that you young people want to liberate me. But however attractive the plan is, it is impracticable because my old body could not stand the hardships of such a journey. Perhaps you heard that I recently got over a serious illness, and I have still not quite recovered.

TORRICELLI   We thought about this too. One of my friends is a physician and would be among those accompanying you and would take care of your health. The itinerary is worked out exactly. From Rome to Venice we have provided for each night's lodging at reliable places. I admit that during the trip we cannot provide you with such comforts as this house offers. But do not forget that at any time you may be transferred to the prison of the Holy Office. I think if one had to choose between the cottage of an honest goat-herd and the prison, the choice would be easy.

GALILEO   My young friend, I appreciate your intentions; but it seems to me that you cannot imagine yourself in the place of an old man. Let us speak no more about that, however, and let us suppose that I would be able to survive the hardships of the trip. Still you did not ask yet whether I really want to leave Rome at all.

TORRICELLI   You just admitted it was a mistake to come to Rome. I thought that this meant that if an opportunity were offered, you would be ready to escape.

GALILEO   You misunderstood me. I feel that I cannot retreat; I have to carry on this fight to the end, even though my chances are much worse than I thought when I came here. If I were to run away, my enemies would be victorious; the cause of freedom for scientific research in Italy would be lost. Just because of you, in the interest of the younger generation, I cannot retreat.

TORRICELLI   Master, I do not understand you. You said earlier that you were disappointed in that you could not count on the aid of the Pope. In whom can you trust? I know that among the Jesuits there are many who know that you are right; but I hope you do not imagine that they would dare to defy the Pope. Recently I spoke with Pater Grienberger and I asked him openly what he thinks about your dialogue.

GALILEO   And what did the good friar answer?

TORRICELLI   It was evident that he wanted to be faithful to his scientific conscience and to the Church, simultaneously. He said that he appreciates your crystal-clear logic and unrivalled knowledge. And although he feels that some of your sentences were composed without enough caution, thereby giving your enemies the opportunity to misinterpret you and thus to turn high-ranking persons against you, still he himself never doubted the purity of your aims. He finds your arguments extremely remarkable, even if he feels that the impulse carried you too far, and even if he himself has some rather serious reservations.

GALILEO   That is really a diplomatic answer: everybody can find in it what he wants. You are, of course, right in that I cannot hope for much help from such cautious friends. Did he say anything else?

TORRICELLI   Yes, something which perhaps can be important: he said that he considers you a good Catholic.

GALILEO   Pater Grienberger knows very well that this is not a question of religion. Don't be misled, my son, when my enemies act against me in the mantle of religion. Though they have followed this tactic from the beginning, and now after many decades of shrewd intrigue have managed to get the Church on their side—against me and against science—nevertheless, the matter in question is really something quite different.

TORRICELLI Who then are your real enemies and why do they hate you?

GALILEO My real enemies are my stupid and incompetent colleagues, the Aristotle-parroting, pseudo-scientists who are not willing to look into my telescope, lest they be forced to revise their false teachings. They hate me because they are afraid of the real method of science. According to my views, the real aim of philosophy is to understand the laws of nature, and this can be attained only by careful observations, and by well-planned, well-analyzed experiments; and these laws can only be expressed with the help of mathematics. On the other hand, what they call philosophy is the firing of Aristotle's quotations at each other.

TORRICELLI I cannot imagine how somebody who wants to understand nature can refuse to employ the scientific method. Surely what is substantial in Aristotle's teaching was attained by him— or if not by him, then by some other Greek scientist—essentially by the same method.

GALILEO Certainly, and I dare say if Aristotle were alive now, even he would turn against the pseudo-scientists harping on his words. But do not forget, these people do not want to understand nature, they are not interested in science, but only in simpering in the gown of the scientist and in getting good salaries. Therefore, their intrigues against me are not surprising at all; I have become accustomed to the fact that I cannot write or say anything without their trying to attack me. These people prefer intrigue to research, and they are better prepared for it too. The trouble is that by doing this they also prevent me from working. I have wasted my best years defending myself against their imputations and lies, and now I am standing here as an old man, and the book that I have been planning all these years is not yet written.

TORRICELLI   If you accepted our plan, then you could write that work which everybody really interested in science has been waiting for so long. I do not understand why you do not want to get out of this unworthy situation. You cannot hope for anything good from your enemies; your friends are unable to do anything in your interest. In what do you still trust?

GALILEO   I trust only in truth. Think it over: as a matter of fact, they do not even know what to accuse me of. My dialogue, the writing of which the Pope himself encouraged, I submitted properly to the censor. It was duly examined from all sides and its publication authorized. They say that the censor lacked caution, that he should not have permitted the publication of the work. But this is not my business, and what can they do against me for that? Of course, they can suppress the dialogue, which I really do not mind since it has been out of print anyway for a long time. If they decide that my dialogue must be burned, I do not know where they will find a single copy. It would be nice if they printed it again to have something to burn. But otherwise they cannot even prove the censor made a mistake. *I adhered strictly to the instructions of Cardinal Bellarmine not to advocate the teaching of Copernicus. In my dialogue I related quite objectively all those arguments which are in favor of the Copernican system, but also those which seem to be against it. Anybody who reads my dialogue can see that I presented the arguments for the immobility of the earth much more powerfully than any one of my silly enemies who cry shame upon Copernicus could have.* It is not my fault if the arguments are not convincing. If anybody wants to blame me, he must first find better arguments for the immobility of the earth. During the hearings thus far, however, I had no occasion to speak about this; they always silenced me, and began to interrogate me again and again about why I did not remind the censor that in 1616 the Holy Office was already dealing with the question. But this is ridiculous; the censor would know that fact better than I. They answered that I should have told the censor what Bellarmine said to me 16 years ago. But he only acquainted me with the mentioned decision. Then they asked whether Bellarmine said only that I should not advocate the Copernican teaching, or that I should not discuss it in any way. However, he did not say not to discuss it "in any way." In connection with this, I still have an unused trump in my hand. *I have a letter written to me by Bellarmine in which he mentions our talk. In it there is stated only that I should not advocate the Copernican theory.*

MRS. NICCOLINI   And if your enemies conjure up some document in which just the opposite of this is stated, what will you do then?

GALILEO   Such a document cannot exist.

MRS. NICCOLINI   It has happened before that documents have been forged.

GALILEO   I do not consider even my enemies to be capable of such vileness.

MRS. NICCOLINI   Do not forget: he who fights against truth cannot be fastidious in choosing his means; he becomes more and more involved in a labyrinth of lies and slander.

GALILEO   No, it is impossible. I am convinced that if I show them Bellarmine's letter, it will finish the whole question. It is time to do so too, because they keep interrogating me about these formal questions. But about what the truth really is—whether the earth, turning on its axis, revolves around the sun, or whether it stands unmoving in the center of the universe—about this we have not spoken a single word. Once I have the chance to speak my mind, I think I can turn the whole case.

TORRICELLI   And were you to have that chance, Master, what would you say? Would you prove to them, that undoubtedly the Copernican theory is the only true one?

GALILEO   I would love to do that, my son, if I could, because I am convinced that it is the truth; but unfortunately I cannot prove it beyond any doubt. I can prove only that the teaching of Copernicus is in accordance with all available facts and no known fact contradicts it. The apparent contradictions can all be easily explained. I have demonstrated that if the earth is moving, we, who are living on it and are moving together with it, cannot notice its motion directly; so our everyday experiences do not refute the Copernican theory. The situation is the same with respect to the spherical shape of the earth. People once hesitated to accept that too. In the age of Dante they said it was against common sense; they referred to their everyday experiences. They said, if the earth were spherical, people on the other side would hang upside down, and would fall off. So much nonsense was talked about the antipodes! Today everybody has forgotten these discussions and people are accustomed to the idea that the earth is a ball. What could they do when they saw that the ships which sailed off to the east returned home, after a time, from the west? This year is the hundred eleventh anniversary of the return of Magellan's ship, "Victory," from its round-the-world trip. We do not yet have such a spectacular proof of the earth's motion; this is the reason it is so difficult to fight for the truth. I can prove only that everything brought forward as a proof against Copernicus is due to misunderstanding or ignorance. *I can prove that it is easier to explain the apparent motion of the sun, the moon and the planets by the Copernican hypothesis than by the Ptolemaic theory. The moons of Jupiter, the ring of Saturn, the sickle of Venus, and a lot of other phenomena which I discovered, support the Copernican theory;* but none proves it. During the hearings the charge was raised that I wrote my dialogue to prove

the truth of Copernicus. When I declared, in answer to this charge, that I did not write it for this purpose, I suppressed only the fact that I could not do so simply because the conclusive proofs were not yet in my hands.

TORRICELLI   But what about the theory of ebb and tide? Don't you think it is conclusive?

GALILEO   When I wrote my dialogue I attached great importance to this question. But I have to admit that reading it again after three years, I am not satisfied with this part. If I were to rewrite the dialogue, I would leave it out, or write it differently.

TORRICELLI   Why? Your explanation of ebb and tide by the double motion of the earth is very convincing.

GALILEO   Do not misunderstand me; it is not that I doubt my findings on ebb and tide. But I think that while an explanation of them by the motion of the earth is easier than other explanations, still this argument is no more conclusive than the others.

TORRICELLI   I see.

GALILEO   I know, now you are wondering whether it was at all worth while to raise so much trouble if I could not solve the question decisively. No, do not protest. I know that this idea is in your mind; it is quite natural. I, too, thought often in the last month, wouldn't it have been better to wait some years until I had found the conclusive proof. But after sound consideration, I answered "no" to this question. I am already an old man, I cannot wait long, perhaps I shall not live to see the discovery of the conclusive proof. I feel that what I can say—even if it does not settle the question—is important enough to be said. I feel also that I am obliged to tell what I know because it may help someone else find the conclusive proof. But I am afraid we are still far from this point. Even the Copernican hypothesis itself needs perfecting because it does not describe exactly the apparent motion of the planets. I did not succeed in explaining the discrepancy between theory and observation.

TORRICELLI Kepler asserts that if we suppose the orbit of each planet to be an ellipse, with the sun at one of its foci, and if we suppose that the planets move not with uniform velocity, but so that the product of the velocity and of the perpendicular drawn from the focus to the momentary direction of the motion is constant, then we get a better agreement.

GALILEO Does Kepler really say that? This surprises me; until now it escaped my attention. But I do not think that such hypotheses are really needed. Why should the planets move just in elliptical orbits? Doesn't this resemble the epicycloids which are used to adjust the Ptolemaic theory to the facts? The hypothesis that the planets move in circular orbits, with uniform speed, is the only one I can explain to myself by mechanics; and it is also the simplest.

TORRICELLI That something is simple does not mean it is true. It was you, Master, who ridiculed those who are unwilling to accept the existence of mountains on the moon—in spite of the fact that if they looked into your telescope, they could see them—because if there are mountains on the moon, then it is not a perfect sphere, and so it is imperfect.

GALILEO   This is, of course, a ridiculous argument. Even more ridiculous is that by which Clavius tried to justify the perfection of the moon: that the valleys of the moon are filled with an invisible material, and so in spite of the mountains we see on it, the moon is still exactly ball-shaped. With equal right I could say that Clavius really has donkey's ears, only they are made from a perfectly transparent and fine material, so that they are invisible, intangible and in no other way observable. As for the ellipses of Kepler, of course one must examine those hypotheses too. If freedom of research is not limited, then in a short time it will be done. In our situation, I think it most important that the Church should not restrict the freedom of scientific research into the question of the earth's motion, or into any other question concerning nature. They say my dialogue upholds the banner of Copernican theory. I answer that the main aim of my dialogue is to uphold the banner of the freedom of science. This is why I wrote my dialogue; it is for this that I suffer all the persecution produced by that work. I am not worried about the fate of the Copernican theory; sooner or later its truth will be accepted. But I am very much worried that if in the present fight I do not win, then for a long time science will be paralyzed, at least here in Italy. What does it help if I myself escape to the Netherlands? Apart from the fact that I can hardly imagine beginning a new life at my age, it would mean that I am giving up the fight before I lose. While the slightest spark of hope lives in me, I will not do this. Please give my best regards to your friends. It is really good to know that there still are people who want to help me.

TORRICELLI   You can always count on me and my friends; we shall do our best. But I am afraid if we keep putting off the realization of our plan, it will be too late. Good-bye, Master, and send me a message if you change your mind about our plan, or if I can help you in any other way.

GALILEO   Good-bye, my friend. I thank you for coming and I thank you for everything you wanted to do for me. Good-bye.

MRS. NICCOLINI   I will show Signor Torricelli out. . . . That Torricelli is a nice young man. . . . Taste these smiling Florentine apricots, Signor Galileo. If one looks at them, one forgets all trouble. I listened to your discussion with great pleasure, though I did not understand everything perfectly. When you have time, I shall ask you to explain certain things to me.

GALILEO   Do so now. I like to talk to you about science, Catherine, because you have a sound, free mind, unspoiled by scholastic pedantry.

MRS. NICCOLINI   Wouldn't you prefer to rest? Aren't you tired after this talk?

GALILEO   Not at all, only I am a bit upset. I am absolutely fresh and will talk to you with pleasure about whatever you want. Tell me what you are interested in.

MRS. NICCOLINI   I did not understand what you said about the teaching of Copernicus: that you are convinced about its truth, but you cannot prove it. If you cannot prove it, why are you convinced that it is true? However, if you have good cause for this, then why is any further proof needed?

GALILEO   That is a thorny question I cannot answer with one or two words; first I have to tell you a few things about the scientific method. But before doing this, I would like to ask you something because I am dying of curiosity. Tell me, how did you find out that your servant was spying on me?

MRS. NICCOLINI   I will tell you what happened, since you discovered it anyway. It struck me that Giuseppe—so the rascal was called—sometimes disappeared for a few hours. Then, last Friday noon when I went to market, I saw him in a doorway, whispering with a Dominican friar. This was, of course, suspicious, but I was not yet sure about its meaning. I thought I should test the fellow. I put one of my falcons into a sack and asked Pater Castelli to send it to us, pretending that it was sent to you. When I heard somebody knocking at the door, I sent Giuseppe to open it. After some minutes I went after him. The falcon was flying around in the corridor, and Giuseppe, with bloody hands was trying to catch it. I was almost sure, but I still had some doubts; perhaps he was only curious. I decided to make another test. I wrote a letter to Archbishop Ascanio Piccolomini in which I gave an account of your health; I intentionally left the letter on the table; after this I poured ink on the floor. I called Giuseppe and asked him to wipe it up, and then I went out to the terrace; but in my little Venetian glass I watched what he was doing. I saw the rascal read the letter zealously and make notes on it. Now I was quite sure of my hypothesis, but for a final control I asked him next day, "Do you know how to read and write?" He answered that he did not know how to write, even his own name. "Get out of my house. I do not need such a blockhead," I said. But really, I do not know why I am tiring you with this long story.

GALILEO   You are not tiring me. From what you said, I see that although you never learned it, you have more knowledge of the scientific method than all the peripatetics in the University of Padova. Because what were you really doing? You observed that Giuseppe disappeared and you wondered what the cause of this could be. When you saw him whispering with the Dominican, you devised a hypothesis—that Giuseppe was actually a spy. Then you did not wait until a new observation chanced to present itself, but rather you planned an experiment with the falcon. You said to yourself: if Giuseppe is a spy, he will open the bag. So it happened. A superficial thinker would have seen his suspicion proved. But you asked the following question: can I not explain the action of Giuseppe in another way, for example by the fact that he was curious? You recognized that although the experiment led to the result you were expecting, it was not conclusive. So you planned another experiment, with the letter. The result was again what you expected. In spite of all this, you made a last attempt; you asked him whether he knew how to read or write. Because he denied it, you were convinced that he was really a spy and sent him off. He who wants to unveil the mysteries of nature has to use essentially the same method. On the basis of observation, one constructs a hypothesis and tries to check it by well-planned experiments. It is not enough to listen to the random words of nature; one has to cross-examine nature. If the experiment does not give the result we expect, then our hypothesis is refuted. But if it gives that result, the hypothesis is not yet proved because one has to ask the question: can I not explain the result in yet another way? If we find another explanation, a new hypothesis different from the first one, then we have to make another experiment to judge whether the first or the second hypothesis is the true one. If the result of the second experiment is again in accordance with the first hypothesis, but contradicts the second, then the last one has to be withdrawn, or at least changed.

Mrs. Niccolini But then this process never ends because one can always find such complicated explanations for all the experiments made. For example, we can explain by his curiosity why Giuseppe read the letter. Of course, this is not enough to explain why he copied it. But I can imagine for this another explanation, for instance, that he liked my style. We can explain that he denied being able to read and write because he was afraid that I would give him copy-work. Does this all mean that a hypothesis on nature can only be disproved, but never actually proved?

GALILEO No. Of course, after every contradictory experiment we can modify the wrong hypothesis, and thus eliminate the contradiction. But every experiment which leads to the outcome we expect on the basis of our hypothesis and which is incompatible with the contrary hypothesis (except when it is modified), corroborates our hypothesis. Many such concordant experiments form in us the firm conviction that our hypothesis is true, even if we do not actually have a conclusive proof.

MRS. NICCOLINI I begin to understand. If I patch an old, worn-out shirt only to have it tear somewhere else, then I realize I must throw it away. But still you have not answered me. How can we ever be absolutely sure that our hypothesis on nature is true?

GALILEO Actually a physical hypothesis on nature can never be proved in the same way as a mathematical theorem, namely by deducing it from certain axioms by a series of logical conclusions. Hypotheses on nature are themselves really axioms, and axioms cannot be proved in mathematics either. One cannot prove the axioms of geometry. One can see that these are right only because the geometry based on them describes correctly the space in which we are living. Physical hypotheses, in general, cannot be proved in a formal way. The only thing we can do is draw conclusions from these hypotheses about observable, experimentally controllable events, and verify these conclusions. But the deduction of conclusions from our hypotheses is done by the methods of mathematics, so that we use our hypotheses as axioms, and from these we conclude with mathematical rigor.

MRS. NICCOLINI Now I begin to understand why mathematics is needed in the study of nature.

GALILEO This is only one of the reasons why mathematics is indispensable for the study of nature. There is another deeper one: the fundamental laws of nature themselves cannot be expressed other than in mathematical formulae. *The great book of nature can be read only by those who know the language in which it is written, and this language is mathematics.* Those who are only gabbling about nature instead of observing it and forcing it, by experiments, to speak, will never know it. But if somebody succeeds in making nature speak to him, then it speaks in the language of mathematics; and if we do not know this language, then we cannot understand what it says. And it is not enough for someone to know this language only desultorily—unfortunately, there are many such people—because then it can easily happen that he will completely misunderstand what nature says to him; and if he wants to tell his own ideas in the language of mathematics, the result will be a miserable stutter. There are many philosophers who have strange—I dare say, barbarous—ideas about mathematics. Today they cannot deny the need for mathematics, but they say that someone who uses mathematics for the study of nature does not need to know it thoroughly. These asses say they need only the final results; they have no time and patience to struggle with the proofs and the exact formulation of the theorems. This is the same stupidity as if somebody were to say: "Let us cut down the leaves and the roots of the tree because we need only its fruits." Whoever wants to enjoy the fruits of mathematics must—whether he likes it or not—accept its way of thought too.

MRS. NICCOLINI I do not understand how somebody can want to use mathematics, and yet be hostile to its spirit. I am only a beginner in mathematics, and I know only as much as you, Signor Galileo, have told me during our talks; so it would be pretentious for me to form an opinion on this subject. Still, I have noticed something. However, I do not want to tire you. You certainly know everything I could say.

GALILEO   Please go ahead and tell me your thoughts; I am very much interested in what you have noticed. Your impartial mind often notices such things that escape the attention of many of my learned colleagues.

MRS. NICCOLINI   I noticed that I do not really understand a mathematical theorem until I understand the proof perfectly. Sometimes it happens that I understand a theorem perfectly only when you have shown me another proof, quite different from the first. When it first happened that you told me an additional proof for a theorem, I admit I did not understand why it was needed, why one proof was not enough. But then I noticed that it is really useful to look at a question from many sides, just as it is useful to look at a statue from different angles. Of course, I understand why someone shrinks from a harder proof; I also was often frightened by a long and complicated chain of arguments which I had to follow step by step. I often felt like a rock-climber who climbs to the top of a mountain between dangerous precipices and who must look only before his feet, taking care not to slip. When he arrives at the top, however, and looks around, the magnificent view is compensation for the hard work. First I undertook to understand the tiresome proofs only in the hope of this sight; but recently I also have found pleasure in the surprising and ingenious steps of the proof, such joy as is found in the most beautiful music. I think the situation is the same with the rock-climber: first he undertakes the tiring trial of strength only in the hope of a nice view; but when he gets used to it, the climbing itself, the defeat of obstacles and the discovery of new grips become for him a source of pleasure too.

GALILEO   You do not know how happy your words have made me. Only a few students in my long life have understood me and the real spirit of mathematics so well. When I tell you something new, I always look into your eyes. I watch for them to light up because I know it means that you understand the point. In teaching, this gleam in the eye always gives me the greatest pleasure. This is the same joy which comes when the fire in the oven, which we are trying to revive, at last flames up. There are teachers who try to teach mathematics by the memorization of rules and by developing a mechanical routine. They are bunglers, and such teaching is not worth much. The real teacher is concerned most with making the student understand; he tries to teach him how to think. Whoever learns only recipes, instead of really understanding what he learns, will not be able to use these recipes correctly because one can count well only by thinking. He who counts instead of thinking generally computes everything in too complicated a way, and often does not count what is needed; so even if in the computation there is no mistake, the result is worthless and useless. I would like to add two things to what you said. First, mathematics is not only useful and even indispensable if someone wants to understand nature or to utilize its powers—for example by building machines—but also it is interesting and beautiful, an exciting and wonderful adventure of the human mind. I think that the beauty of mathematics is not a subsidiary, accessory thing; it is one of its basic features. Truth is always beautiful and beauty is always true. The old Greeks knew this very well. Those who have barbarous notions about mathematics do not understand this: either they are blind to the beauty of mathematics, or if they see it, they are suspicious of it. They think that beauty is a luxury which is superfluous; and when they turn their back on her, they think they get nearer reality. They simper in the role of the practical man and arrogantly despise those who penetrate the real spirit of mathematics. However, nothing is so unreasonable as this arrogance which really exposes their own impotence. This is the same

example, if you drop something, it will fall in the same way whether the ship stands or moves. Of course, this would not be true if the speed or the direction of the ship changed. But as long as the ship moves uniformly in a straight line, you cannot notice it from the cabin. Of course, if the cabin has a window through which you can see the seashore, you will be able to judge whether the ship moves with respect to that shore. But if you are out in the open sea, and you see only another ship, and you notice that your ship is moving with respect to the other one, you again cannot know whether this happens because your ship moves, or the other ship, or both.

MRS. NICCOLINI I understand that. But by the Copernican theory the earth does not move in a straight line; rather it moves around the sun. Isn't this similar to when the ship changes its direction, which, as you said, can be noticed in the closed cabin?

GALILEO It is hard to notice if the ship changes its direction slowly; we feel only sudden changes. The earth turns around the sun once a year; so during a few hours, the direction of motion changes only a little bit. This makes the observation hard.

MRS. NICCOLINI And what about its rotation on its own axis? As I understand it, according to Copernicus, the earth makes a complete rotation each day. Can't we somehow notice this motion directly?

GALILEO I see from your question that you well understand what type of conclusive proof I am looking for. However, as I said, I have not found it yet; but I trust that science will find it soon.

MRS. NICCOLINI I have another problem: I did not completely understand what you said about the laws of nature being written in the language of mathematics. It would be clearer if you gave an example.

GALILEO Come to the window, please. Look at this ball; I shall set it free; observe how it will fall to the ground. Observe it as it falls. What did you notice?

MRS. NICCOLINI It seems to fall faster and faster.

GALILEO You are right, but how does it gather speed? There is a marvellous, simple regularity. If you consider the distances the ball covers during equal periods, they are in proportion to each other, like the odd numbers: that is, it covers during the 2nd second 3 times the distance of the 1st second; in the 3rd second, already 5 times the distance; in the 4th one, 7 times, etc. In other words, the falling body does gather speed uniformly—its movement is uniformly nonuniform. Earlier the scholastics were dealing with such motion; but they did not use mathematics, although this motion cannot be really understood without it.

MRS. NICCOLINI This is really very interesting.

GALILEO Wait a minute, I have not yet finished what I want to say about the falling bodies. What I have said so far can also be expressed by saying that the velocity of the body increases proportionally with time. Let us now observe the distance the falling body covers from the beginning of fall until an arbitrary instant. If we denote the distance—what is covered in the 1st second—by a, then, as I said, in the 2nd second the distance is $3a$; so the sum of the distances covered in the first two seconds is $3a + a = 4a$. Do you remember what I said about the distance covered in the 3rd second?

MRS. NICCOLINI Of course I do: $5a$, and so during 3 seconds the sum is $4a + 5a = 9a$; in the 4th second—as you said—the distance gone is $7a$, so during 4 seconds the total distance gone is $16a$.

GALILEO So the falling body covers during 2 seconds the distance $4a$, during 3 seconds the distance $9a$, during 4 seconds the distance $16a$. Do you see some regularity in this?

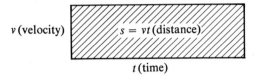

Motion with constant velocity

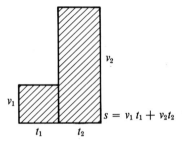

Motion with piecewise velocity

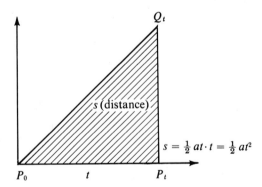

Motion with velocity changing at a uniform rate

Mrs. Niccolini   It seems to me that the distance covered from the beginning is proportional to the square of the number of seconds. Is it really so?

Galileo   Yes, and it is true not only when the time considered is equal to 1,2,3,4, . . . seconds, but also in general.

Mrs. Niccolini   How can this regularity be proved universally?

Galileo   That is very simple. Draw a straight line. Choose a point P_0 on this line, which will correspond to the instant when the motion started. Then every point P_t of the line L lying to the right of P_0 corresponds to an instant t after the motion started. In each such point P_t draw a perpendicular to the line L and select on it the point Q_t the distance of which from P_t is equal to the velocity of the falling body at the instant t corresponding to the point P_t. As the velocity increases proportionally to the time, the points Q_t will lie on a straight line starting from P_0.

Mrs. Niccolini   That is clear, but how can one see from this figure the total distance covered?

Galileo   This is simple: the distance covered until the instant t is equal to the area of the triangle $P_0P_tQ_t$.

Mrs. Niccolini   Why is that so?

Galileo   If the velocity is constant, the distance covered is equal to the product of the time and the velocity. If a horizontal segment represents time, a vertical segment velocity, the distance covered is equal to the area of the rectangle having the mentioned segments as its sides. If the velocity changes, the situation gets more involved, but the distance will still be equal to an area. For instance, if the velocity is constant for some time and then suddenly changes to a higher value and remains at that, then the distance covered will be equal to the area of a domain consisting of two rectangles. If the velocity changes often, but remains constant between two consecutive sudden changes, then the distance covered will be equal to the area of a domain consisting of many rectangles. If the velocity starting from O changes continuously at a uniform rate, then the distance covered will be equal to the area of a triangle. To understand this you have only to see that a triangle may be considered as composed of infinitely many, infinitely thin parallel rectangles of different heights.

MRS. NICCOLINI That is really marvellous. Will your book on the mathematics of motion deal with this question?

GALILEO Yes, and also with many other similar questions. Just as it can be predicted where the falling stone will be after 2 or 3 seconds, so can it be shown that a stone thrown away in any direction will fly on a parabolic course. This point is interesting not only in practical situations, but because through it I can show how different motions can be combined. Actually I do not understand why, when Ptolemy had already tried to compute the apparent orbits of the sun, the moon and the planets—all of which are observed day by day, year by year—nobody, except perhaps Archimedes, examined thoroughly what happens when a stone is dropped or thrown away. Moreover, I say—even if I am again suspected of heresy—that *here on earth, motion follows the same laws as it does in the heavens.*

MRS. NICCOLINI So the whole universe is like a big clock in which one can exactly compute how the wheels turn, from the smallest to the biggest.

GALILEO These marvellous regularities form only one chapter of "Nature's Book"! There are also many irregularities, unpredictable random events.

MRS. NICCOLINI What do you mean?

GALILEO Think of the new stars which occasionally—for example, 60 years ago—appear suddenly in the sky. For some years they shine more and more brightly, and then they disappear just as suddenly as they came. Think of the sunspots which revolve around the sun near its surface. Sometimes they grow, sometimes lessen, appear, swirl and disappear. The universe is not similar in every respect to a mechanism; in some respects it is more similar to an unpredictable, capricious woman.

MRS. NICCOLINI From what you said, it seems to me that in the book of nature there would be some chapters not written in the language of mathematics because they deal with unpredictable events.

GALILEO You are mistaken, Signora, but I can well understand this because so far only the first steps towards a mathematical description of chance have been taken; though to do so is possible, as I have shown recently by a very simple example.

MRS. NICCOLINI What was this example?

GALILEO The game of dice, this old, but still popular game of chance. If we throw a die, how it falls depends completely on chance. If the sides of the die are labelled by the numbers 1, 2, 3, 4, 5, 6, and we throw the die once, then we can say only that the number we see will be any one of these six. But if we throw a die many times, then we observe a certain regularity: every one of the six numbers will be thrown approximately just as many times. It is still more interesting if we throw two dice at the same time, and we add the numbers we see on them. What can we expect?

MRS. NICCOLINI That is quite clear; the sum can be every number from 2 to 12.

GALILEO Yes, but these 11 possibilities will not happen equally often. Most often 7 will be obtained, in about 1/6th of all throws; after it come 6 and 8, each will be obtained in about 5/36th of all throws; 5 and 9 will be in 1/9th of all instances, while 4 and 10 will be obtained in 1/12th of all instances; and both 3 and 11 will be obtained in about 1/18th of all throws. Finally, the sum 2 and 12 will be thrown in 1/36th of all instances.

MRS. NICCOLINI This sounds strange. Why does it happen?

GALILEO There is a very simple reason. *We can throw 4 as a sum in 3 ways: namely as the sum of 3 and 1—either the first die shows 3 and the second 1 or conversely; and also as the sum of 2 and 2. But we can throw 12 only in one way, so that both dice show 6. Therefore, among the sums, 4 will occur about 3 times as often as 12.*

MRS. NICCOLINI Sometime I will try playing dice by these rules. Do you think one can win a lot of money with this knowledge?

GALILEO The game is fair, if the rules are fixed so that no player is in a more favorable situation than the others. Of course, if the rules are not fixed correctly, then one player can win a lot if he has the money to play until the laws of chance prevail to his advantage.

MRS. NICCOLINI I never thought that mathematics was the basis even of games of chance. What is this branch of mathematics called?

GALILEO It is so new that it has no name yet. It could be called the calculus of probability.

MRS. NICCOLINI How is it that I have not yet heard about it?

GALILEO Mathematicians, accustomed to dealing with what is regular and exact, until recently shrank from dealing with chance because it did not seem to be their concern. The authority of Aristotle acted in the same direction: according to him, mathematics was to deal with the unchangeable. And what can be more freakishly changeable than chance? But there were other, much older prejudices: it is an ancient custom to see in chance events, like the throwing of dice, the flight of birds, and the irregular forms of the liver of a sacrificial animal, manifestations

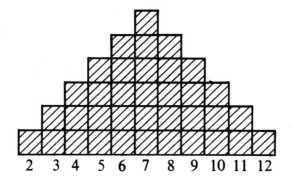

$2 = 1 + 1$
$3 = 1 + 2 = 2 + 1$
$4 = 1 + 3 = 2 + 2 = 3 + 1$
$5 = 1 + 4 = 2 + 3 = 3 + 2 = 4 + 1$
$6 = 1 + 5 = 2 + 4 = 3 + 3 = 4 + 2 = 5 + 1$
$7 = 1 + 6 = 2 + 5 = 3 + 4 = 4 + 3 = 5 + 2 = 6 + 1$
$8 = = 2 + 6 = 3 + 5 = 4 + 4 = 5 + 3 = 6 + 2$
$9 = = 3 + 6 = 4 + 5 = 5 + 4 = 6 + 3$
$10 = = 4 + 6 = 5 + 5 = 6 + 4$
$11 = = 5 + 6 = 6 + 5$
$12 = = 6 + 6$

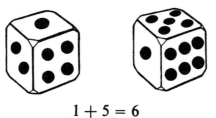

$1 + 5 = 6$

of the will of the gods. All this caused a holy shuddering in people faced with random events; most of them felt it almost blasphemous to try to explain such events with the human mind. However, my point of view is that man has a brain in order to use it.

MRS. NICCOLINI   I like the way mathematics—though I know only as much as I have heard from you—makes the most complicated things simple; by the light of the torch of mathematics, many things which were difficult and not understandable become so crystal-clear and simple.

GALILEO   Yes, that is true. But I must tell you, mathematics sometimes shows that the apparently simple things are really very complicated.

MRS. NICCOLINI   What do you mean, Master?

GALILEO   I will give you only one very simple example. On this paper let us write the integers from zero onwards, as follows: 0,1,2,3, ... Let us imagine this series of numbers continues to infinity. Now let us mark among these numbers the square numbers. You see, as we go ahead we meet fewer and fewer square numbers because the distances between them become longer and longer.

MRS. NICCOLINI   Really, the distances are 1,3,5,7,9, . . . just the odd numbers.

GALILEO   Similar to the distances covered by the falling stone. But now tell me: if I say there are less square numbers than numbers in general, am I right?

MRS. NICCOLINI   Certainly.

GALILEO   Now do the following: write down again the series of integers, and write under each number its square. In the second line there are only square numbers, aren't there, and each occurs only once?

MRS. NICCOLINI   Yes.

GALILEO   Under every number stands another, and so in the lower line there are as many numbers as in the first one. Do you still say that there are fewer square numbers than numbers in general?

o 1 2 3   4   5   6   7   8   9 10 11 12 13 14 15 16....
o 1 4 9 16 25 36 49 64 81....

MRS. NICCOLINI   This example has confused me completely. What is its point?

GALILEO   That *what is true for finite things is not necessarily true for infinity.* Actually, Zeno noticed this already—remember his paradox of the Stadium? He noticed that one can project the points of a segment $B'C'$ from the point A on a larger segment BC so that to any point P' of the smaller segment there corresponds a point P of the larger segment. Only he did not know that this paradox also happens in connection with the integers.

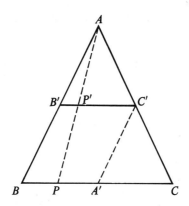

MRS. NICCOLINI   In the same way one can show that, in general, there are as many even numbers as integers, in spite of the fact that only every second integer is even.

GALILEO I see that you really understand what I say. One can tell if somebody understands something thoroughly when he is able to transform or modify it for himself; in a word—to create it anew.

MRS. NICCOLINI That is really true. If someone can cook only by following recipes, she is not really a good cook. The good cook modifies recipes freely, gives more spice or less, to such an extent that what she cooks will be a different dish every time.

GALILEO The good cook makes experiments like a scientist—and she can do this freely without being suspected of heresy.

MRS. NICCOLINI Signor Galileo, while you were telling me so many interesting things, night arrived. I think it is time for you to go to bed. I am sorry that I kept you up so long. Probably it tired you to explain all these things to me.

GALILEO Oh, not at all, our talk has pleased me very much. I forgot my situation during it.

MRS. NICCOLINI Really, you should not think about it so much.

GALILEO Do you always ask me questions about mathematics to distract my mind from my troubles?

MRS. NICCOLINI I hope you are not angry about that, are you? Believe me, even if I have such thoughts, I am really very much interested in these problems. However, it seems to me, Signor Galileo, that you can read not only the book of nature but also the human soul if you want to. I do not understand why you do not use this knowledge of yours against your enemies; you could defend yourself better and would irritate them less.

GALILEO To read your angelic soul is just as pure a joy for me as to search the wonders of nature. But I do not like to read the soul of my enemies; only the pig likes to poke in dirt.

MRS. NICCOLINI Nevertheless, if you overcame your loathing and tried to read the thoughts of your enemies, I guess you would

84

change your opinion about that plan of Torricelli and his enthusiastic friends.

GALILEO   You also suggest that I should run away? Do you think I should accept their offer?

MRS. NICCOLINI   The only reason I do not answer the question with a simple "yes" is that I do not know how realistic their plans are and whether they would really succeed? In your place, Signor Galileo, I should try to find out. If the plan is realizable—I am not at all convinced about that—then you should accept it. I did not want to interfere, but now, since you asked me, I must give my opinion.

GALILEO   You also do not trust that I shall win?

MRS. NICCOLINI   You said you trust only in truth. I agree that truth sooner or later will prevail, only I am not convinced we will still be alive when that happens. You said that the charges are unfounded and they cannot prove them. It seems to me that you are committing an error: you think the Inquisition uses the same high standards in checking proofs as you do in science. But let us not speak about this. Perhaps I am too pessimistic. Now it really is time to go to bed. I hope tonight you will sleep as well as you did last night.

GALILEO   Last night I dreamed that the room where I sat suddenly began to fly, higher and higher, far up into the clouds, out into empty space. You cannot imagine how happy a feeling it was to look from such a distance down to the earth—which became smaller and smaller, and shone in the dark sky by the light of the sun just as the moon shines. I saw it moving, turning majestically around the sun and around its own axis too. I was happy as perhaps I have never before been in my life. I saw with my own eyes the motion of the earth! I looked through the telescope which previously I used to search the sky; now I looked down with it from the sky to the earth; I directed it to Rome. It was a very good telescope, much better than any I ever made, so I even recognized faces. Imagine, I saw Inchofer and Pasqualigo, those two dark-souled asses, walking by the River Tiber and discussing something. I pushed a button on my telescope and suddenly I heard their conversation; they talked about the motion of the earth and asserted that it was a false and heretical doctrine. But the earth did not bother about their silly chatter; it continued on its orbit with dignity, and turned on its axis carrying them with it. They continued to slander me and Copernicus; it was so ridiculous that I broke out in such laughter that my tears were flowing. I laughed so hard that I woke up.

MRS. NICCOLINI   That is really a nice dream. Perhaps tonight you will dream about an age in which even the small children learn in school that the earth moves around the sun.

GALILEO   I dream about this often when I am not asleep, and I am sure this age will come soon. The progress of science cannot be stopped. But sometimes I have doubts whether this age will be really as happy as I imagine. Will this age not have its own prejudices and dogmas? Will there not also be stupid, envious, spiteful and intriguing men? Will such people not try to stain the honor of honest men by base slander? Will there not still be parasites on the flourishing green tree of science?

MRS. NICCOLINI   Certainly there will be such worms then too. But there will always be men for whom truth is more important than everything else, and these will look back to our age and will see that Galileo Galilei stood above his contemporaries by two heads, and they will proudly declare themselves to be his students and the followers of his work.

POSTSCRIPT

POSTSCRIPT

An optimistic author does not write a preface to his book, because he is confident that it will speak for itself and he is convinced that the readers will understand what he wants to say without any additional explanation. While I am an optimist, I felt that in the case of this book, if not a preface at least a postscript was needed on the aims of the author and on the considerations which led him to choose the literary form of the dialogue. I add these remarks in the form of a postscript because I really want them to be read after the dialogues.

The interest in mathematics and its applications is increasing year by year in every country among an increasing number of people. I have been asked several times to give popular talks on mathematics; on such occasions I noticed that many people were primarily interested in finding out what mathematics really was, what its specific method consisted of, what its relation to the sciences and humanities was and what it could offer to those working in different fields. I found also that those who attended such lectures on mathematics or who were ready to read books on mathematics written for non-specialists usually wanted simply to broaden their outlook rather than to acquire specific mathematical methods. Even those who actually needed a knowledge of mathematics for their work, before deciding to study seriously a particular part of mathematics, wanted to find out what they could expect from it, especially since the study of mathematics is not easy for those unused to it.

While talking about mathematics to non-mathematicians I encountered quite a number of prejudices, misunderstandings and misconceptions, not only among people whose main interests and activities are quite far from mathematics but also among those who through their profession have a certain knowledge in some part of the field. This is really not surprising as those people who have some knowledge but do not have sufficiently broad vision or sufficiently deep insight, are most inclined to make false generalizations. I found also that the principles of mathematics and of its applications are often disputed even among mathematicians and many questions in this field are subject to controversy.

These circumstances convinced me that there exists a real need for a discussion of the basic questions of mathematics and its applications in a manner which while comprehensible to non-specialists, yet presents these problems in their full complexity. I realized that it would not be an easy task to make such questions understandable to the general public, therefore I searched for a special method to bring abstract problems nearer to the layman. This search led me to experiment with the Socratic form of a dialogue. The Socratic dialogue presents thoughts while they are being created and dramatizes ideas. By so doing it keeps the attention awake and facilitates understanding.

I chose as the central theme of the first dialogue the question "What in fact is mathematics?" I consider the discussion of this question especially important because the teaching of mathematics in elementary and high schools is still far from giving a clear-cut, correct and up-to-date answer.

In this dialogue I tried to follow as closely as possible the method and even the language of the original Socratic dialogues. Socrates himself is the main actor and the discussion takes place in the period when mathematics, in the sense that it has been understood ever since, was born; thus mathematics is presented to the reader "in statu nascendi." In the dialogue Socrates applies his peculiar method of discussion: by the phrasing of his questions he leads his partner to understand the issue. Thus a Socratic dialogue is not the clash of two points of view; rather the participants try to find out the truth together. By a logical analysis of the concepts involved they arrive at an answer to the questions step-by-step. During the discussion the participants often make statements—sometimes in a quite categorical form—which they later realize to be false. Thus a Socratic dialogue is an organic whole and its real meaning can be understood only if one reads it from beginning to end, if possible without interruption. All these features make a Socratic dialogue lively and vivid, and so I found this form particularly suitable to my aims.

I had still another reason for choosing this form: it is my firm belief that the Socratic method is basically cognate with the mathematical method. In this belief I was very much strengthened by the recent fundamental research work of Árpád Szabó, which has thrown quite a new light on the origin of Ancient Greek mathematics.

The first dialogue was published in Hungarian [1] in 1962. In 1963 a French translation appeared in Les Cahiers Rationalistes.[2] In 1963 I presented this dialogue as an after-dinner talk to the meeting of American Physicists in Edmonton, and an English version was published both in the Canadian Mathematical Bulletin [3] and in Physics Today,[4] and was reprinted by the journal Simon

[1] Dialógus a matematikáról, Valóság, 3, 1–19, 1962.

[2] Un dialogue, Les Cahiers Rationalistes, 33, No. 208–209. Janvier–Février, 1963.

[3] A Socratic dialogue on mathematics, Canadian Mathematical Bulletin, 7, 441–462, 1964.

[4] A Socratic dialogue on mathematics, Physics Today, December, 1964, pp. 1–36.

Stevin [5] too. Since then it has also appeared both in German [6] and Portuguese [7] translations.

The favorable reception of the first dialogue both among mathematicians and among non-mathematicians encouraged me to continue experimenting with this genre. A second dialogue was first presented at the University of Toronto in 1964 and appeared in English in the *Ontario Mathematics Gazette* [8] and later in *Simon Stevin*.[9]

Since in the first dialogue I had discussed the relation of mathematics to reality only in a general philosophical sense, in the second I wanted to make central a more detailed discussion of the applications of mathematics. It was logical to choose Archimedes as the chief character of such a dialogue as his name even in ancient times was inseparably connected with such applications. The historical frame of the second dialogue, however, did not allow me to say all that I wanted about this controversial topic.

Thus I felt I had to write a third dialogue, the chief character of which was Galileo, the first thinker in modern times who fully realized the central importance of the mathematical method in discovering the laws of nature, and who propagated his conviction with great force. The second and third dialogues thus complement each other, and also the first. They are, however, essentially different from the first in form and style. Archimedes and Galileo do not, of course, use the method of Socrates: instead of guiding their partner to guess their thoughts, they express them themselves. Thus

[5] A Socratic dialogue on mathematics, *Simon Stevin*, 38, 125–144, 1964–1965.

[6] Sokratischer Dialog, *Neue Sammlung*, 6, 284–304, 1966.

[7] A matemática—Um Diálogo Socrático, *Gazeta de Matemática*, 26, No. 100, Julho–Dezembro 1965, pp. 59–71.

[8] A dialogue on the applications of mathematics, *Ontario Mathematics Gazette*, 3, No. 2, 28–40, 1964.

[9] A dialogue on the applications of mathematics, *Simon Stevin*, 39, 3–17, 1965.

I had to dispense with the main source of inner tension which the Socratic dialogue provides. I tried to compensate for this loss by putting these dialogues in extremely decisive historical situations, the dynamics of which were inseparably connected with the issues of the dialogues and would thus amplify their tension.

Featuring Archimedes and Galileo made it possible to touch in these dialogues on much more specialized mathematical topics than were discussed in the first one, especially on such ideas which originated with Archimedes and Galileo themselves; I tried to incorporate in some form or other most of their famous achievements.

In this connection I must say a few words about how I dealt with historical facts. In all three dialogues I tried hard to avoid every sort of anachronism. I was careful not to attribute to my characters any such knowledge of mathematics (as well as of other things) which they could not possibly possess at that time. However as both Archimedes and Galileo were pioneers whose ideas and way of thinking were not only far ahead of their time but also are modern even when measured by present day standards, I was not prevented from including in these dialogues everything I deemed important to say. Of course, in order to avoid anachronism I had to restrict myself mainly to examples from elementary mathematics; I could thus go into infinitesimal mathematics but only as far as Archimedes and Galileo did themselves. This restriction, however, had certain advantages because it forced me to avoid examples which would have been too difficult for the non-mathematician.

I did not, however, interpret the requirement of historical faithfulness so rigidly as to attribute to my characters only such views and ideas which they certainly possessed; I felt free to attribute to them views and ideas at which they may have arrived, particularly if these were logical developments of such ideas with which they were definitely familiar. In cases, however, where it is known they had erroneous beliefs, I felt compelled not to hide the fact. Thus, for instance, it is known that Galileo thought that the planets move in

93

circles around the Sun and he did not understand the role of gravitation; so Galileo speaks about these questions accordingly. On the other hand, I thought it admissible to make such bold conjectures as, for instance, that Archimedes arrived at certain ideas which are nowadays classified under cybernetics and that he planned a machine for sieving primes.[10] I cannot support such conjectures by any document, and of course do not consider them as well founded; the only thing I claim is that it is not unthinkable that these conjectures are true and, furthermore, that the facts at our disposal are as insufficient to disprove these conjectures as to prove them. I thought that "poetic license" entitled me to use such hypotheses as these.

As for the historical background of the second and third dialogues, I kept to the facts in every essential point. The only exception, where I departed consciously from the facts, is in the second dialogue where King Hieron is directing the defense of Syracuse in the siege of the year 212 B.C., while in reality he died three years earlier. However, both dialogues contain the description of hypothetical events about which we have no definite knowledge, but which are not contradicted by known facts. This is the case, for instance, with the plan of helping Galileo to escape: we do not know whether Torricelli and his friends really had such a plan, but it is not at all impossible.

The essential content (though usually not the wording) of some sentences in the dialogues is either directly attributable to my characters or attributed to them by their contemporaries. This is the case, for example, when Socrates talks about himself,[11] Archimedes

---

[10] Such an apparatus was first described by D. H. Lehmer (A photoelectric number sieve, *American Mathematical Monthly*, 40, 401–406, 1933).

[11] See for example "The Apology of Socrates" (*Great Dialogues of Plato*, translation by W. H. D. Rouse, edited by Eric H. Warmington and Philip G. Rouse, Mentor Books, 8th printing, New York, 423–446, 1962).

about his method [12] and Galileo about the language of the book of nature.[13] Such sentences (and only these) are printed in italics.

I have tried to present the personalities of my characters as faithfully as possible. In the case of the third dialogue, the drama of L. Németh influenced me greatly: I took from it, among other things, the idea of presenting Torricelli and Signora Niccolini.

For those who want to study the historical background of these dialogues, a selected bibliography is added which does not aim at completeness; it contains only such books I found particularly useful in the collection of my material.

I hope this postscript makes clear what my aims were in writing these dialogues. It is up to the reader to judge how far I was able to realize my intentions.

ALFRÉD RÉNYI

---

[12] See the letter of Archimedes to Eratosthenes (*The works of Archimedes, with the method of Archimedes,* edited by T. L. Heath, Dover, New York, 1960). See particularly the following sentences on page 13: "Certain things first became clear to me by a mechanical method, although they had to be demonstrated by geometry afterwards, because their investigation by the said method did not furnish an actual demonstration. But it is of course easier when we have previously acquired by the method, some knowledge of the question, to supply the proof than it is to find it without any previous knowledge."

[13] See particularly in the letter of Galileo called "The Assayer" (*Discoveries and opinions of Galileo,* translated with an introduction and notes by Stillman Drake, Doubleday Anchor Books, New York, 237–238, 1957), the following sentences: "Philosophy is written in this grand book, the universe, which stands continually open to our gaze. But the book cannot be understood unless one first learns to comprehend the language and read the letters in which it is composed. It is written in the language of mathematics. . . ."

SELECTED BIBLIOGRAPHY

SELECTED BIBLIOGRAPHY

First Dialogue

Rouse, W. H. D. (trans.), *Great Dialogues of Plato* (Mentor Books, New York, 1962).

Szabó, Á., Wie ist die Mathematik zu einer deduktiven Wissenschaft geworden, *Acta Antiqua Acad. Sci. Hung.*, **4**, 109–152, 1956.

—— Die Grundlagen der frühgriechischen Mathematik, *Studi Italiani di Filologia Classica*, **30**, 1–51, 1958.

—— The transformation of mathematics into deductive science and the beginnings of its foundation on definition and axioms, *Scripta Mathematica*, **27**, 27–48, 1960.

—— Anfänge des Euklidischen Axiomensystems, *Archive for History of Exact Sciences*, **1**, 37–106, 1960.

—— Der älteste Versuch einer definitorisch-axiomatischen Grundlegung der Mathematik, *Osiris*, **14**, 308–369, 1962.

Second Dialogue

Clagett, M., *Greek science in antiquity* (Collier, New York, 1955).

Heath, T. L., *The works of Archimedes with the method of Archimedes* (Dover, New York, 1960).

—— *A manual of Greek mathematics* (Dover, New York, 1963).

Third Dialogue

Armitage, A., *The world of Copernicus* (Signet Science Library, New York, 1947).

Drake, S., *Discoveries and opinions of Galileo* (Doubleday, New York, 1957).

Fermi, L. and G. Bernardini, *Galileo and the scientific revolution* (Fawcett World Library, New York, 1965).

Galilei, G., *Dialogues concerning two new sciences* (Dover, New York, 1914).

—— *Dialogue concerning the two chief systems—Ptolemaic and Copernican* (translated by Stillman Drake, foreword by Albert Einstein. University of California Press, Berkeley and Los Angeles, 1962).

Geymonat, L., *Galileo Galilei* (Einaudi, Rome, 1957).

Santillana, G. de, *The crime of Galileo* (Mercury, London, 1961).